My Lord and the Angel
An Encounter at Harvington Hall

My Lord and the Angel

An Encounter at Harvington Hall

by
Rosie Martin

Grant Books, Worcestershire 1997

Acknowledgements

I would like to thank Fr. Geoffrey Tucker for making this book possible, Peter and Lucy Hancock for editing, Michael Hodgetts for proof reading and the photographs. Eileen Heard has put my words into typescript for which I thank her.

Fr. Geoffrey Tucker and Michael Hodgetts have been a constant source of help and encouragement and I dedicate this book to them.

Rosie Martin,
London
September 8th 1997

Photograph Acknowledgements

The photographs on pages 4, 12, 16, 21, 67 and 72, taken in 1896, are from the Stone Collection in Birmingham Reference Library and are reproduced by permission of Birmingham Library Services. The remainder are from a series in the Hall archives which were taken in 1914 and 1917.

Cover illustration

From a painting of 1878 by Lieut. Colonel Henry Howard F.S.A., now at the Hall.

ISBN 0 907186 26 2

*Typeset in 11 on 13 point New Baskerville
and printed in Great Britain
produced by*
Hughes & Company
Kempsey, Worcestershire, England

*Published
by*
Grant Books
The Coach House, Cutnall Green, Droitwich, Worcestershire WR9 0PQ

Contents

Foreword

IN 1921 a ten-year-old girl came across and explored a mysterious and almost derelict moated manor-house in Worcestershire. There she met a venerable figure who was addressed as 'My Lord' and was so like her childish image of God that she thought he was God. Now aged eighty-six, E. Rosie Martin has written a vivid and imaginative account of the childhood adventure which has shaped the whole of her life.

This encounter with 'My Lord' at Harvington Hall started her 'enduring quest'. Throughout her life she returned when she could to her beloved Harvington. Always in her mind was to write about her experience and the way it shaped her life.

Rosie Martin

Part I

Breaking and Entering

Nowhere in this part of England imparts so strong a sense of sadness, of muted suffering and spiritual endurance.

Sometimes the whole recusant experience of fire and torture, muddled loyalties, fines and penal laws, seems to be summed up here.

In its various entrances, its big windows commanding the approaches, and, of course, its amazing honeycomb of priest-holes, the L-shaped mansion has a perpetual air of nervous readiness about it, as if a justice's posse were even now going to sweep in along the drive.

Jonathan Keates 1979

Chapter 1

Stairs and Passages

THE GREATEST man who ever lived on this earth was a carpenter – Jesus Christ. He came as the Light of the World. In His wake came another carpenter whose light shone in dark and hidden places. His name was Nicholas Owen. Both these carpenters died brutal deaths; one to light the flame of Faith and the other to keep it burning.

Nicholas Owen, known as 'Little John' because he was small and walked with a limp, was a Jesuit lay brother and servant to Father Henry Garnet S.J., the Superior of the English Province.

'Little John' Owen was an inspired contriver and constructor of many ingenious hiding-places for priests in the great recusant houses all over the country so that all who adhered to the faith of their fathers could hear Mass and receive the Sacraments. He saved the lives of many who hourly courted death for their devotion to Jesus Christ.

This is not a religious book (so many works have been done on the subject already and as most of the writings are deeply sincere I can neither presume nor aspire to the standard of excellence attained by their authors) but a tale of old brick walls, dim corridors leading into rooms long since forsaken, and secret hiding-places. This is a story of one great house – my beloved Harvington Hall.

I am now a very old woman; one of the few people living who knew and loved Harvington as it was before the task of restoring it was undertaken, when it stood desolate and decaying, its walls wrapped in a thick blanket of ivy and weeds, surrounded by the sinister dark waters of its moat.

As I stood on the bridge leading to the main entrance under an arch, a deep love was born in my immature ten-year-old heart, a love for an ancient house that has endured throughout the passing of the years. This over-whelming feeling of fascination was tinged with sadness and an inexplicable desire to find the answer to questions that had never been asked before. At that time I was far too young and ignorant to analyse my emotions, so I did not understand that I was embarking on a quest – a quest seeking the fulfil-ment of a dream.

Shafts of golden sunlight lit up the parts of the red walls that were visible. Something inexpressible, ineluctable shone in the glow of the ivy, and some-thing indefinable and invisible in the atmosphere set my pulses racing as I stood there feeling like Moses must have felt when he stood looking at the burning bush. Unlike that gentleman, however, I did not remove my

The East side

footwear, because I intended to do a 'nosey-parkering' act inside the house.

Getting into the house presented no problem. A door on the left-hand side under the main gateway was hanging crazily on its hinges and, after a bit of a heave from me and a loud creak from it, into the house I stepped in great style. For a minute or two I stood inside the doorway waiting for my heart to stop looping the loop. The light was dim due to the ivy over the windows. A few golden spears of sunlight pierced the ivy in places, but everywhere else was silvery grey like shadows wearing shrouds. The air was dank and carried the smell of old plaster, dust of many years and generations of spiders. Perhaps I had a spot of dry rot in the place where my heart was meant to be, but there I stood breathing in the air and loving it as if it had been Chanel No. 5.

Then I moved forward and picked my way through to chaos that only time and neglect knew how to arrange. Avoiding the debris scattered about the floors, I began my grand tour of Harvington. Since I was only ten years old, I was unblissfully ignorant concerning the history of the house and its collection of secret hiding-places. Blissfully unaware at the same time that a heavy adult would have probably put his foot through an unsafe floorboard. In some rooms the floorboards were very wide, with a gap of about a quarter of an inch between them and, although it was summertime, a cold little breeze carrying a whiff of stagnant water wafted me on my way as I walked across them.

It seemed such a queer house; so many winding staircases and passages with odd steps in unexpected places because the floor levels differed from room to room. There were so many doors seeming to have nothing behind them, secluded corners and mysterious corridors, all thickly festooned with spiders' webs hanging like great shawls of filigree lace. The juicy-looking occupants of these webs I will not describe in detail in case you are having your tea or reading this in bed.

By this time I was lavishly decorated in cobwebs myself, and I was beginning to feel more than a little confused. Something was definitely strange about the house; something missing, as if the heart of the place had been torn out. And it had. The main staircase was gone, leaving a wide void and small curly flights of newel stairs arranged on either side of it. There was no great hall to complement the missing stairway; just a solid uncompromising wall.

The twisting stairs I ascended stopped at the first floor, abandoning me in a maze of doors and dim passages, and though I did not know it then, I was standing on the threshold of the oldest part of the house – the low range of buildings in the middle of the east side – lovely gracious old rooms with more than a hint of sadness pervading the atmosphere. Fallen plaster, piles of rubble together with scars and defacements of time, did nothing to dispel the essence of dignity and elegance lingering in those forgotten rooms.

One room in particular fascinated me. This was a very large room with the dimensions of a banqueting hall. There it was, standing in its brickwork underwear because it had been stripped of its panelling and, if the handsome wainscot on the door was anything to go by, the walls must have looked magnificent before the house was left to die.

Standing just inside the doorway, my back and the palms of my hands pressed against the wall, I was overwhelmed with a sense of belonging to this house. A feeling it was, stretching far beyond the comprehension of a child.

Standing there, eyes almost closed, I became aware that the room was filled with living memories floating on invisible wings. Spirits from a distant past bestowing a blessing and imparting an urgent request to my unenlightened mind. After a while I turned and rested my cheek against the wall and in that enchanting moment, my quest began. What the quest was to be about or what kind of a quest it was to be, I did not know. I did not realise then how long the answers to my questions were going to take. **Almost a lifetime!**

A shadowy passage took me to the stairs leading to the upper regions, and to my surprise, parts of the second floor were swept and tidy and I began to wonder if the house was occupied in some part. I remembered a stout door just beyond the gateway when I was trying to find a way in; it appeared to be firmly locked, but the law against trespassing, I felt, was made for everybody but not for me. So, with the nonchalance of a consolidated jellied eel, I pressed on regardless with my inspections of the second-floor rooms. Quite unexpectedly, I came to a halt on the threshold of a small room that had such a holy feeling about it, that I convinced God lived in there, so I did not go in. God knew too much about me, I thought. In those days, I thought God was a very old gentleman wearing a nightshirt, and having a long – incredibly long – nose and masses of floating white hair and curly whiskers to match. By His side, He would have His recording angel with notebook in one hand and pencil in the other, and God would be saying to him, "Write that down! Record that outrage in capital letters – mind your spelling – and cross your t's like a Christian!" No, I did not dare to go right inside that little room. I did not see God in there, but I knew He was there just the same. My aunt did send me to Church and Sunday school, but I never honoured either place with my appearance because I did not have a hat nor any Sunday clothes. Everyone else wore their Sunday best; little girls in dainty dresses and starched white pinafores, domed with straw hats and dangling ribbons; boys squeaking and squelching about in sturdy leather boots that had iron tips attached to the heels to make them last longer, and wearing tight trousers that made their eyes water. Their noses ran ad lib on Sundays because the boys did not dare to use their Sabbath day cuffs on them. The grown-ups, too, had their cross to bear, creaking about in a haze of boredom and the nauseating smell of camphor balls. Once, though, I did see a magic lantern show; a black and white flickering affair it was, and the heroine of the story was an angelic child dressed in rags and her hair hanging down in great sausage curls; her eyes, of course, were as big as saucers, fringed with lashes long enough to sweep the garden path. It was so beautiful that I did not know what to do with myself, and when a rose actually dropped out of heaven and lay at her feet, even though she was in an attic, I was so overcome that I fell off the form I was sitting on, and my betters sent me out of the hall for (I quote) 'playing about'. Being expelled from the magic lantern did not bother me, and I am sure that I was not the only one to be deprived of the Word of God that evening. How could any child over six believe that a rose could fall out of the skies, through the roof and then through a ceiling? Strangely enough, five stairs higher, I found myself in a maze of attics getting my come-uppance for being so scoffy about the rose. None of those attics had ceilings at all, and looking up I saw the wooden ribs that were supporting the roof which was full of gaping holes revealing patches of heavenly blue sky.

In a somewhat thoughtful frame of mind, I at last turned and made my way towards the door I had come in by, and after losing my way several times and stopping for a last glimpse at the lovely large room, I found myself standing on the bridge near the gateway in the late afternoon sunshine. My hair was full of cobwebs, and my boots were full of feet, but my heart was in heaven as I turned and began the long trek across the meadows to home.

The East side during restoration, 1931

Chapter 2

Aunt Mary

A LMOST EVERY family has an Aunt Mary. She is usually a spinster going about the business of living in an inconspicuous manner, listening to the tales of woe of those seeking a quiet tongue and ears that would not flap. A lady with broad shoulders to carry the burdens of others, leaving room for the hard-done-by to cry on. Anyone who needed money automatically went to Aunt Mary and she was always there to sort out problems and minimise anxieties. From helping to settle arguments and complaints, to giving a penny to a child with a guy, Aunt Mary was never known to fail. These Aunt Mary ladies never bend anyone's ego by telling them to go to hell. No. They send birthday cards and Christmas presents, but the only flowers they ever get is when they shuffle off to Buffalo; and I can tell you why. When nobody needs a loan from Aunt Mary or wants to borrow her Sunday hat, or wallow with them in a sink of self-pity, and pick them up when they have fallen down and chipped their knees, they don't give her as much as a passing thought. They stuff her into the rag-bag of their minds and only bring her out again when something disagreeable drops into their breakfast egg.

Aunt Mary lived in a small cottage on the outskirts of Kidderminster. My father died in the battle of Mons, so my mother joined the W.A.A.C. and went to France after depositing me, at the age of five, on the bounty of my Aunt Mary, who made no protest apart from observing that it was a pity my mother had not joined the Camel Corps instead of the Women's Auxiliary Ambulance Corps. Even when World War I was over, my mother seemed to be in no hurry to collect her left luggage; my Aunt Mary was cluttered up with me, steering me through my whooping cough (and heaven knew how loudly I could whoop!), seeing me through my measles and dealing with my mumps.

The cottage we lived in had been left, with a small annuity, to Aunt Mary by her mistress whom she had served with devotion for many years. She had also inherited a large white Persian cat with a magnificent tail and enormous blue eyes. Her name was 'Oo-la-la', and the little mongrel dog, 'Ichee-Koo', came with them because his owner, who had been head gardener on the lady's estate, had also died. Ichee-Koo was a friendly, sporty little fellow who looked like a cross between a doormat and a scrubbing brush. I loved them both dearly, but my Aunt Mary adored them; they reminded her of happier years when life seemed to be so full of purpose and promise, when she had felt the contentment of being needed. So she lavished all her love and care on Oo-la-la and Ichee-Koo. Not that they entirely took out the loss and loneliness from her heart; I would often see a stray tear creep from the corner of her eye when she looked at either of them. They wanted for nothing and the wind was not even allowed to blow on them. Oo-la-la loved as much adulation as she could get, sitting aloof and lofty on her cushion until someone or something upset her apple cart. Then she could outshine all of us when it came to swearing and snarling. Now Ichee-Koo was different. Dogs can speak with their eyes and he made it quite clear that he preferred to go philandering round the village rather than sit on a cushion with a ribbon tied in a bow round his neck. He did not care to be groomed either, and when Aunt Mary tried to cuddle him, he made a queer little grunting noise that sounded to me suspiciously like "Oh gawd!"

The third of her three protegés stood on two legs, and had straight black hair that hung in rats' tails about her shoulders, and a pair of light grey eyes that seemed to be focusing on some far-away object most of the time, according to Aunt Mary.

I was not as lucky as the other two. Many a time I pinched one of Ichee-Koo's big square dog biscuits and squatted on the kitchen doorstep to enjoy the feast, whilst he stood near watching me out of the corner of his eye. On the days when he had not been rolling in the mud, it was possible to see what colour he really was. His undercarriage was mainly white, his flanks tan, his saddle was black, his head was a gold colour livened up with white blotches and pink nose, but his tail was his crowning glory. It was long and feathery and coloured with dashes of black, brown, white and fawn, looking as if it had been put together as an afterthought with all the bits left over.

Arriving home after my first visit to Harvington, I found my Aunt Mary seated at the table, book propped at a convenient angle against the teapot, absolutely engrossed in what she was reading. She was one of the world's most avid readers; she would read anything from 'Peg's Paper' to the Holy Bible with relish, and through her profound love of the printed word, she had acquired an outstanding amount of general knowledge and a command of the English language that was extremely wide and very picturesque. My Aunt Mary could come out with any quotation from the Bible to meet an appropriate situation, but was quite expert at embellishing them with a few words of her own. Some of our neighbours said she was crazy, but I thought she was clever and a most comfortable person to live with because, although she fired questions at you, she never gave you time to answer before she hurled the next one. By the time she had run out of breath, she had completely forgotten what it was she had wanted to know.

That evening, however, feeling certain that she could tell me about that lovely, lonely old house I had found that day, I interrupted her in the middle of her next question.

"Aunt Mary – "

"And how did you get into that state – what?"

"Do you know an old house on an island that doesn't belong to anyone and is falling to bits?"

"Where? There used to be several hereabouts, but they are all gone now."

"No. This one is still there. I have seen it – I went in – "

"They turned Johnny Peffer out of hell for telling lies!"

Nothing in the world was going to convince my aunt Mary that I was speaking Judgment Day truth, so I let it pass and began to wheedle until my whining got on her nerves and she capitulated and told me as much as she knew about the old house. Taking a hunk of bread and sprinkling it liberally with sugar, I sat myself opposite to her and hung on every word. I was so excited that I dipped pieces of my bread into the sugar bowl until my aunt Mary noticed what I was doing and quietly substituted the salt cellar for the sugar bowl.

"That old house is quite a long way across the fields from here," she began, "and it belongs to a family called Throckmorton. Harvington Hall – that's the name of the old house – came to the Throckmortons by marriage. Lady Mary Yate's grand-daughter had married Sir Robert Throckmorton of Coughton Court in Warwickshire. The Throckmortons made the last alterations to the house, starting off by knocking down two sides of the courtyard, leaving the east and south sides and part of the north block."

"Why did they pull half of it down?"

"How should I know? They didn't ask my permission and it happened over two hundred years ago. Anyway, after 1800 the Throckmortons never lived there: after all, they had beautiful Coughton Court."

"And they just left Harvington Hall to fall to bits?"

"Not altogether. A set of apartments in the North Tower was well maintained so that members of the family or friends could pay short visits from time to time."

Aunt Mary got out of her chair and went outside to fill the kettle.

"Aunt Mary!" I yelled after her, "Tell me some more!"

Aunt Mary decided to put on her funny act. "Once upon a time there were three bears: father bear, mother bear and ba – Oi, put that salt cellar down! If you tip that salt in the sugar, I'll take you apart and I'll scalp you!"

The temptation to do just that with the salt had been overwhelming but I nobly resisted because I wanted my aunt Mary to tell me about the people who had once lived in that Harvington Hall. She was the kind of person who knew what was what, without adding any embellishments. To get her to part with a bit of information was no easy task, but I made up my mind to try, and when she came in from the washhouse-cum-scullery with the teapot, I began my wheedling campaign.

"Dearest auntie, won't you tell me some more about that old house?" I pleaded, "I'll let you read my 'Tiger Tim's Weekly'."

"Fancy a great girl of ten reading it. Anyway, I found out where you hid it, so I have read it."

"Auntie, darling, I'll scrub the kitchen floor."

"That'll be the day!"

"I'll do the washing – I'll dust the coal – I'll sieve the ashes – I'll clean the windows – "

"Oh yes? When will these wonders happen? When donkeys wear high hats and cows carry handbags? Or when lemons grow on aspidistras?"

"I have got this week's 'Magnet' – I haven't even read it yet."

"I have!"

She sloshed out two mugs of tea and pushed one of them over to me and sat herself down facing me. So I played my last card; by sheer will, I powered my face to put on my most heart-rending expression of pathos and began to sing a very sad song.

When my aunt Mary's nose was not stuck in a book, her ear was wedged halfway down the horn of the gramophone listening to sad songs like 'Do you remember sweet Alice, Ben Bolt' and 'The Gypsy's Warning', but aunt Mary simply loved the sorrowful songs of Stephen Foster, and I shared her admiration for all his songs and with her I shared and deplored his untimely death on Skid Row with only thirty-eight cents in his pocket.

However, I set about the business of the moment. I took a deep breath and placed my hands across my heart and began –

"Thou wilt come no more, gentle Annie,
Like a flower thy spirit did depart,
Thou art gone, alas, like the many
That have bloomed in the summer of my heart.
Shall we never more behold thee?
Never hear thy winning voice again?
When the springtime comes, gentle Annie,
When the wild flowers are scattered o'er the plain."

Now I was no singer; I never was, but my voice was not the object of the operation's success. I was relying on Ichee-Koo, and bless his heart, he did not let me down. He could not bear to hear me sing, so up went his nose, pointing to the ceiling, open like the gates of heaven came his jaws and out poured the most unearthly howls that would have put a pack of wolves to shame. As I put more and more expression into the words, Ichee-Koo's "Ow-oooooooo's" grew louder and made a good accompaniment to my vocal attempt.

Aunt Mary should have been crying into her tea – she always wept when she heard 'Gentle Annie', but there she sat laughing her head off, while a tear or two dropped into my own mug.

View from the South-East

Aunt Mary picked up a large spoon and gave me a smack on the back of my hands cutting short my performance in its prime. Ichee-Koo let out one last magnificent "Whooooooooo" by way of an encore, and closed his little jaws with a snap, reminding us of an excommunicating bishop stopping the bell, blowing out the candle and shutting the book with a certain amount of high dudgeon.

Peace thus restored, aunt Mary observed that I should have chosen 'The Old Folks at Home' rather than 'Annie'.

"Why?"

"You want to know about the people who used to live in that old house and hereabouts."

"Why don't you tell me about them?"

"Because you are not really interested, you are just a little nosey-parker who never goes to church on Sundays, and besides, you have got fleas and dirty knees and you don't love Jesus!"

I turned haughty. "I joined the Band of Hope and I have signed the Pledge!"

"Oh yes, I remember it so well," agreed my aunt, "you joined a week before they held their Christmas party, and you have not set foot inside the place since."

There was nothing I could say in reply to that, so I got up, collected the mugs and carried them out to the scullery; and like the gentleman of the Psalms, I moaned and complained and made a great noise, especially with the mugs. They were made of enamel and used to having somebody's pique taken out on them.

Back in the living room-kitchen, aunt Mary had cleared the table and put on the red plush cloth and was taking out her latest piece of literary genius. It was a mystery take entitled 'Handsome but Dead'.

"Would you like me to tell you who did the murder?" I asked sweetly, indicating the book.

"You are a blackmailing little hussy. Put a light to the fire and I will tell you about some of the people who lived there many years ago."

So the fire of sticks lighting up the room (we always had a little fire of sticks, even in summer), Oo-la-la on her lap, me squatting at her feet with Ichee-Koo's head on my lap, we took a little trip to the distant part.

"Before the Throckmortons owned Harvington," began my aunt reflectively, "it belonged to the Pakington family, who were staunch Roman Catholics. Queen Elizabeth and, later, King James were determined to stamp out Catholicism in England. They thought the best way of going about it was to hang, draw and quarter any priest who was caught saying Mass for the people and administering what was known as the Sacraments. Without the Mass, the Catholic religion could never have survived in England."

"What was Mass?" I asked deeply interested.

"The Catholics believe that it is the sacrifice of the body and blood of Jesus Christ, so that He could stay with the world after His mission was over."

"That was a good idea."

"The Catholics only wanted to practise their faith," aunt Mary said very seriously, "but bigotry and hatred on the part of those who had given up their religion led to the most diabolical acts of cruelty. But while it brought out the evil in some, it brought to light the devotion, the incredible courage and the endurance of the many."

This took a few minutes of consideration, but aunt Mary was warming up nicely to her subject. We were not Catholics, but the lady who had been aunt Mary's mistress for all those years, had been one, and she told my aunt many things about the Reformation, the Penal Laws, Recusants and Pursuivants; facts handed down from her ancestors.

I stretched across Ichee-Koo and threw some more twigs on the fire whilst my aunt told me about some of the people who had once lived in the old Hall.

"Lady Mary Yate, who outlived her husband, her son and her grandson, was the last Pakington to live permanently at Harvington Hall. She was a kind and gracious lady and above all things she was devoted to the old faith and she sheltered many a persecuted priest in her house so that her friends and servants could hear Mass and receive the Sacraments. She and her friends in their own quiet way helped to keep the light of faith burning in those days of priest hunting, brutality and bloodshed."

Aunt Mary told me many things about the Pakingtons and their friends, the Habingtons, the greatest Catholic family in Worcestershire. About John Habington, Queen Elizabeth's Cofferer to the Household who built Hindlip House just before his son, Edward, was hanged for his complicity in the Babington Plot, while his other son, Thomas, was pardoned by the Queen, probably because she was his godmother. Yet it was Thomas's wife, Mary Parker, who was suspected of writing the famous letter to her brother, Lord Mounteagle, warning about the 'terrible blow' of the Gunpowder Plot.

As the twilight deepened into darkness, my aunt's voice grew weary and she at last fell silent while I stored all the things she had told me in the untidy treasure chest of my mind. Even the bits that were beyond the comprehension of a ten-year-old.

Chapter 3

My Lord and My Dear

WITH THE coming of the school's long summer holiday, I was free to visit my lonely mysterious house surrounded by its ancient trees. And on one of my frequent visits, I met God.

There he stood in the glory of the morning. That heavenly one-day-in-a-lifetime morning. Not the God of the long nose pointing an accusing finger, but a God who had been to the barber's, and who had discarded His long nightshirt together with His beard and was wearing a long black kind of dress with hundreds of scarlet buttons running in a straight line from His neck to the hem. Round His neck He wore a beautiful chain with a crucifix hanging from it. In one hand, He held a black leather book with gilt edges to the pages; the other hand He raised to beckon me closer had a large ring on one of the fingers that glinted in the sunshine.

Standing there in front of Him, in the general inspection, I noticed that at least ten little buttons near His neck were not properly fastened, and I was amazed because I thought God would have been rather more pernickety about detail. So when He asked me who I was, all I could find to say was, "Who does up all those buttons?", and His reply was, "I do. But you see, I don't undo them all."

This sounded a bit like cheating to me, but it made the atmosphere between us a little more comfortable. After all, He knew all about my little 'ways' so I was not averse to learning about some of His.

When I told Him that I knew He was God, He laughed and assured me that He was not God, but looking at Him steadily for a moment or two, the assurance wore off. Of course He was God.

Doing His best to stop laughing, He explained that there was a bit of God in all of us, and this I found very difficult to believe. If there was a bit of God in me, it was a very tiny piece. He had only to ask my aunt Mary.

My new friend walked through the gateway leading to the house with me at His heels, and crossing the courtyard, He opened a door and I followed Him through a dim corridor at the end of which was a thick door which opened on to another bridge spanning the moat.

Crossing the moat, we walked round the house following the wall that encircled it until we came to a deep green stretch of pasture fringed by a group of tall old trees. Some trees had fallen during the march of time, and we selected a trunk to sit on in a shady convenient kind of a place with a view of the house. God placed His book carefully on one end of the tree trunk and

First floor landing

I put my brown paper bag down with equal care on the other end of the trunk. Then I sat myself beside it, probably looking like a frog on a rockery, but He perched elegantly at my side.

When He spoke, His voice reminded me of Gitchee Manito the Mighty when he stood on the red pipe stone quarry and told all the Red Indian tribes to jump into the stream and wash the war paint from their faces. Oh yes, this one who was sitting beside me was God right enough.

He said, "Now, my little off-white angel, are you going to tell me who you are and what brings you here?"

At first I could think of nothing to say, but when I eventually found my tongue, I assured Him that Harvington Hall was my house and I loved it and always visited it when I was able to get away from my aunt Mary.

He told me that Sir Robert Throckmorton, who was a friend of a friend of His, had not only given Him permission to spend a few weeks at the house, but had lent Him a cleaning woman. He added that His sister was also staying at the house to look after Him. Did you know that God had a sister? Neither did I.

After a short silence between us, He looked me in the eye and in a serious tone of voice, asked me if I had ever found my way into the house, and when I replied with a most enthusiastic "Yes", God became even more serious. Taking one of my grubby paws in His hands, He gazed very earnestly into my face as He said, "Child, promise me that you will never, never go into that house by yourself again. Not ever."

Although His voice was gentle enough, there was an undertone of firmness attached to it and I knew that I would never break a promise made to Him. So I nodded my head and stared down at my boots so that He would not see my face go all sloppy.

"You see, Angel," He explained, "Harvington Hall is very old and very neglected and part of it are not safe. It is a house that guards many secrets, many sad memories and hiding-places where you could get lost and never be seen again."

To stifle the ache that had crept into my heart, I reached for my brown paper bag and took out my big green apple and offered Him a bite. He took a bite, then I took a bite, and when we had eaten about half the apple, a funny thought came into my head. I thought we looked like a dressed version of Adam and Eve sitting on the Tree of Knowledge instead of standing beneath it. He asked me what I was laughing at, and when I told Him I was thinking about Adam and Eve and the servant, He said, "Don't you mean Adam and Eve and the serpent?"

At that exact moment, a figure came dashing across the grass towards us. She was wearing a large white apron and a little mob cap. I did my best not to look smug.

Recovering her breath, she said in a rich fruity Irish brogue, "Me Lord, will yiz be afther comin' in to ate – it's sure not gettin' 'ot at all, at all!"

"Coming at once," He told her, "and Bridie, lay another place at table. We have a visitor."

Bridie took one look at me, cast her eyes upwards, folded her hands across her ample stomach and said, "Jesus, Mary and Joseph!"

God said, "No, Bridie, not the Holy Family. They can't manage to come today."

When the young woman had about turned, He held out a hand and helped me to slide off the trunk of the Tree of Knowledge.

"Never mind Bridie," He said as we walked towards the house, "she is not really taking the name of the Lord in vain. You see, she is au fait with all the angels and saints up above."

The lady who looked after God was a truly lovely person; she reminded me of Grace Darling, Florence Nightingale and a touch of Mary Pickford, but she had one great fault. She was absolutely obsessed with the idea that hands should be washed before partaking of a meal, so she told Bridie to escort me to the bathroom. This really annoyed Bridie, who grumbled all the way round and all the way up to where the washing arrangements were. She was not actually grousing at me. She was asking somebody named Oliver Plunket what he thought the world was coming to, and then she had a go at most of the holy occupants of heaven. Then she had a go at me, "Worra yiz afther doin' 'ere?"

Haughtily I eyed her up and down. "Playin' me harp," I told her. Whereupon, hearing this, Bridie lost her temper and, calling me a saucy little coween, she thrust a bar of yellow soap into my hand and told me to wash my ugly face. Only she did not use the word 'face'.

Now I was not rude. I was never rude to anybody bigger than myself, so all I said was that she was a mahogany-handled, silver-knobbed, brass-tipped cow and a sitter on other people's unmade beds. But I was not rude. In fact, I was repeating something I had read in one of my aunt Mary's books.

With a kind of a howl, Bridie gave the back of my hand, which was still clutching my brown paper bag, such a resounding smack, that my dinner fell to the floor; first, my tired-looking piece of kipper, followed by a sad and downtrodden-looking slice of bread and dripping. The two spring onions were too far gone to put in an appearance. I bent down and reverently replaced them in the bag and when I looked at Bridie, she was crying tears as big as peanuts. "Holy Mother of God, I'm sorry!" she wailed.

"That's quite all right," I assured her.

She snatched the yellow soap from my hand and replaced it with a beautiful piece of mauve soap that was pure bliss on my face and hands. Then she brushed my hair with a nailbrush.

Arm in arm, we descended the stairs, walked round and at last we reached the dining room, looking like Lilian Gish on the arm of Edward E. Lee.

Although I say it as shouldn't, my behaviour was beautiful; no knife found its way to my mouth because I was well aware that peas would not stay put on the blade, and the piece of linen by the side of my plate which they called a serviette was not a handkerchief. I had a narrow escape here, because I thought it was.

The room in which we were sitting was a handsome one, and the sun streaming in through the window danced on the polished walls filling the place with a rich golden glow. It was so clean and cosy that I asked if we were in a house next door to the Hall.

The lady, whose name was 'My Dear', explained that it was the North Tower of the old house, all that was left of the north side that had been demolished many years before. She went on to tell me that the owners had kept the rooms in good repair because from time to time members of the family spent periods of time there.

Lunch was over, grace said, God asked us to excuse Him whilst He retired to say His Office, and when He had departed, I asked My Dear what His 'Office' was that He was going away to say.

She was thoughtful for a moment or two, then she said, "He is talking to God."

This was decidedly astonishing. "But how can He? He is God. If you talk to yourself, people say you are mad."

Me Dear gave me an especially lovely smile. "He is not God, child, but he is a servant of God. People call him 'My Lord'."

'My Lord' sounded very good to me, and I said it over and over again to myself. But he would always be God to me.

When My Lord returned about an hour and a bit more later, I was sitting on a stool in front of My Dear holding a skein of wool stretched between my hands whilst she wound it into a ball. He asked me if I would care to accompany him on a tour of the lonely neglected part of the Hall. Could a duck swim! So he raised his voice and actually bawled for Bridie, who came jingling across the passage to replace me on the stool. I asked why Bridie clinked when she ran and he explained that it was her piety rattling because she was wearing at least half-a-dozen holy medals on a chain. I looked pointedly at his cross and chain, and reading my thoughts, he told me that he never ran unless absolutely necessary, and that at all times he did his best not to let his piety rattle.

Seeing the house with My Lord that afternoon, I noticed many details about the building hitherto unobserved by me. Even to me it seemed to be a lopsided kind of shape, and when I pointed this out to my escort, he told me that two wings of the house had been demolished many years before the

Throckmortons had finally abandoned it. By this time we were standing in the courtyard and looking at a wall on our left, which he said belonged to the main block of the house.

"Beyond that wall," he said, "there was once a magnificent staircase and a large hall known as the great hall. They are gone now."

"What is there now they have gone?" I asked.

"Just a wall dividing the courtyard from the garden. That is the reason why so many doors on the landings are fastened and can't be opened."

"I would have liked to see the big hall," I told him sadly. "Isn't that where they all ate?"

"Yes, Angel," he agreed in a whimsical tone of voice, "they ate right enough. They began dinner just before noon and kept at it until about three, and at four o'clock they had supper."

My Lord knew all the obliging little doors hiding beneath curtains of ivy and we soon found the site whereon the great hall and staircase had been.

He pointed to the ground. "This," he said, "was the marsh, the floor of the hall."

"Why was it called the marsh if it was the floor?"

"Because it was in a disgusting mess. The floor was made of stamped-down earth and it was covered with reeds and rushes from the moat. When new rushes were needed, they were strewn over the old ones. When the trestle tables were set up, the eating began, bits of food, bones, gobs of fat and unmentionable things were thrown under the tables where dozens of cats and dogs snarled and spat and used many a lavish leg belonging to a guest as a modern dog now uses a lamppost, or in the case of cats, a rallentando from various sections of the hall bid well to split the ear-drums. The hawks on perches near their owners shrieked blue murder. Yet nothing could compare with the racket that issued from the table where the squires and pages sat at meat, drowning the blowyings and pipyngs of the minstrels. Above the champing, the burping, the smacking of lips, the guzzling and the gurgling mingling with arguments and bawdy laughter, ushers walked up and down the hall and in between the tables, yelling at the top of their voices, 'Speak softly my masters, speak softly, softly.' Pages had to be watched carefully and admonished not to drink wine with their mouths full, not to sag at the table so their heads would not hang into the dish; that never at meals must they pick their nails and their noses and never, never pick up their plate and lick it."

All this time I had been holding my brown paper bag, but now my grip tightened on it as, putting a hand under my elbow, he led me into the house.

The first thing I noticed was a strange eerie humming kind of noise as we began to mount the narrow winding stairs that seemed to be reaching to heaven.

The stair hide

My Lord looked into my face seeking my reaction to this creepy phenomenon, but I was not frightened; I was fascinated.

"It is only the wind coming through the holes in the roof and having a chase in and out of the rafters," he assured me, but I knew the sound was the voices I had heard on my first visit to the banqueting hall which would, in years to come, be known as the 'Great Chamber'.

We came to a halt on the second floor landing and found ourselves looking at a set of five steps leading up towards the garrets. The two middle stairs were definitely rickety. My Lord stood in front of this small flight of stairs and he made a north, south, east and west sign; then he joined his hands and closed his eyes, bowing his head and saying words so softly that I could not hear what it was that he was saying.

Then to my amazement, he leaned forwarded and folded the uprights and treads of the middle stair right back to reveal a cavity beneath the flight of steps.

There was just room enough for My Lord to squeeze through and help me to scramble down beside him. This tiny place contained another door leading to a little chamber.

"Do you ever say your prayers?" my companion asked me as we looked down into this small chamber.

"Only when I want something," I replied.

Down there it was dark and very cold, but My Lord produced a torch from one of his pockets and handed it to me, whilst he picked up a candle from somewhere on the floor and lit it.

The candle flame shone extra brightly, and stood motionless in its holder in My Lord's hand, shedding a golden glow over the quiet little room. The faint sighing sound from above us, the stillness and silence surrounding us, made an atmosphere beyond all things earthly and beyond finite comprehension as I stood spellbound at the side of my wonderful new-found friend.

The floor of the room was in shadow and when I shone the torch on it, I noticed that it was covered with rushes and in one corner lay the remains of a mattress. Not much of this mattress was left by the hand of time and a year later, when the hall was damaged by vandals, the remnant was torn to scraps and scattered.

A gentle nudge from My Lord brought me back to the world of 'now' from the world of 'then'.

"Whose bed was that?" I asked, pointing to it.

"Among many others," he thoughtfully replied, "this little room was the refuge of Father John Wall, a Franciscan who was the last priest to be hanged in England."

Inevitably, I had to know why Father John Wall was hanged. "Had he stolen sheep?"

"No, Angel, he didn't steal sheep, but he saved a good many and led them back to the fold."

"So they hanged him."

"Yes, my Angel, they hanged him."

"I want you to tell me all about him."

Before he could answer, I suddenly noticed a chink in the wall nearest to me and by stretching up as far as sheer will-power would permit, I put my eye to the hole and found that I was looking down into what I called the banqueting hall.

My friend said it was 'The Great Chamber' and he went on to explain why most of the great houses had them.

"By the middle of the fourteenth century, the lord and lady of the manor began to take their meals upstairs in the room where they slept, and gradually they turned these apartments into great chambers, installing beautifully painted panelling and ceilings. A withdrawing room and bedroom usually adjoined the Great Chamber, but even if the lady of the house was tired of letting her shining countenance be a source of inspiration to her entire household, she did not get much peace, because the few privileged, and the many who considered themselves to be so, soon found their way up to the Great Chamber. Eating in the Chamber was a great and extravagant affair on special occasions; there always was a yeoman of the buttery to take up the beer, a yeoman of the pantry to bring up the bread and a huge dish of salt which he placed on the left of the lord with three ceremonial bows. Next would come the gentlemen Sewer and Carver. These two were thoroughly washed by the yeoman of the ewer. The carver was given napkins on which to wipe his knife before cutting 'sayes' from all the loaves of bread on the lord's table. Ceremonial 'sayes' were taken in front of the lord as a precautionary measure against poisoning. When all this was done, the carver cut 'sayes' of meat and fish and poultry, taking great care to never put more than two fingers and one thumb on the flesh. Then the 'sayes', having been swallowed, the lord's hands were washed and dried amid much kissing and bowing and scraping, and the meal began."

Here, of course, I had to butt in and ask what the sewer was doing whilst the carver was performing his duties with the 'sayes', and I was told that he had done his 'sayes' already in the servery and was in the chamber to assist the carver.

"Why did they taste the food twice over?"

"Because nobody trusted anybody in those days. Not even their own grannies."

There was nothing I could say to this, so my friend added, "We have been in here quite a long time and if we don't go back to our own baronial hall for tea, Bridie will give us the rounds of the kitchen twice over."

Before we left the little secret room, My Lord knelt by what was left of the mattress and bending forward, he kissed the small bed that had given some ease to many an aching body and a brief spell of peace to many an anguished mind.

I knelt down beside him and I kissed the mouldering mattress, and, closing my eyes, I learnt to pray with my mind and my heart.

Whilst My Lord was fitting the stairs back into their original position, I popped into the Great Chamber and laid my cheek against the wall where I had rested it before, but this time I raised my eyes to the chink in the wall near the ceiling where Father Wall could look down upon the gathering below.

"Father Wall," I told him with my heart, "I'm going to be told all about you."

At that precise moment, a rich fruity voice came bawling up the stairs from the direction of the buttery. "Holy Mother of God! All ye holy martyrs and widows and hermits! Will yiz be afther gettin' in for yer teeeea!"

"She's forgotten the Little Shepherd of Kingdom Come," observed My Lord, as the sewer and the carver went in to their teeeea!

There was a beautiful loving aroma of baking when we reached the living quarters of the house, for My Dear had been busy during our absence. Seven big balls of wool stood smugly in a row on a table near the window, and in the centre of the tea table stood the most handsome cake I had ever beheld outside a baker's shop window. It was a lovely dark brown colour with lots of cheeky cherries peeping through the top. I stood looking at it, shuddering with anticipation until Bridie, who was tinkering about with the teapot, reached out and gave me a dig in the ribs and pointed upwards. I understood the gesture, so I dashed out of the room, round the corridor and up the stairs. Never was a pair of hands washed with such speed! Bridie was still tinkering with the teapot when I returned.

There followed, after a brief session of bread and jam, the cutting of that heavenly cake, and when a hefty wedge landed on my plate, I was so delirious with anticipation and joy that I would not have called the Queen so happy. Then, apropos of nothing, a picture came into my mind. In that picture I saw my aunt Mary with Oo-la-la on her lap and Ichee-Koo stretched out on the rug with his head resting on her feet. I put the piece of cake that was en route to my mouth back on the plate.

Three pairs of eyes were watching me in astonishment. My Lord said gently, "What is the matter, Angel?"

"Do you think I could take it home?" I asked, "I'm always taking Ichee-Koo's biscuits and this morning I pinched a little bit of Oo-la-la's kipper, and there's me aunt Mary – she never gets very much."

My Lord's voice was kind of husky as if something was stuck in his throat

The Great Chamber

as he said that I was to eat my cake and that aunt Mary and company would have some as well.

My Dear reassured me by telling me that she had already made another for me to take home, and Bridie, who had poked her head round the door to ask about hot water for more tea, heard what the lady said, and without waiting for me to utter a word of thanks, she did it for me, surpassing any eloquence that would have passed my lips.

"Ooo!" she shrieked, raising her eyes heavenwards, "The blessedly heavenly saint! May every hair on yer head turn into a wax candle to light yiz to glory!"

A suppressed guffaw came from My Lord, but when I looked across the table at him, he was innocently stirring his tea, but when Bridie's back was turned, he pointed a long finger at me and raised an eyebrow. I shook my head and pointed to his sister who was having trouble trying to keep a straight face.

When at length I found my tongue, I told them about my aunt Mary and Oo-la-la and Ichee-Koo.

They wanted to know about my mother, but I could not tell them very much, for in five years I had seen her about half a dozen times at the most. She wrote often enough and sent aunt Mary the money for my keep. That was all I knew.

After tea, I took my leave of My Dear and Bridie, but My Lord left the house with me and accompanied me three parts of the way home.

He told me about Father John Wall, the last priest to be caught and hanged in England. He was not captured at Harvington Hall, although he had spent a number of years there, ministering to the household and surrounding districts. Father John Wall was the eldest son of a great and noble family and heir to a large estate and much land, but he had chosen to serve the Divine Master in the footsteps of St. Francis who had loved all things little and poor.

"The Almighty is not a small grocer. He does not deal in small packets of tea; He cares for the whole consignment. That is why we say 'Our' Father and not 'My' Father."

I considered it time to interrupt.

"Is it wrong to be holy in private?" I was getting a little confused by this time.

"No," he said quietly, "but it is very difficult."

We took a little rest on a stile that was wearing a big notice that told us that
ALL TRESPASSERS WILL BE PROSECUTED
In my ignorance, I took it to mean that offenders would be executed. I was thrilled at the thought!

My Lord went on to tell me of the life of that wonderful Franciscan who, like St. Francis before him, gave up all ties with family, loved ones and all possessions that could have given him a soft comfortable life, to work in God's vineyard, walking every hour of every day in the shadow of arrest and certain death.

He paused and waited for the everlasting "Why?", and after I had obliged, he continued, "You see, Angel, since the beginning when God created the world, He asked His people to offer sacrifices up to Him."

"Oh, yes," I chimed in, "I have heard about Cain and Abel. God was pleased with Abel's sacrifice, so the smoke went straight up to heaven, but the smoke from Cain's sacrifice went all over the place."

My Lord nodded very gravely, so feeling that he needed further enlightenment, I explained that Cain was jealous and killed his brother Abel.

"Yes," he agreed, "Abel died because of his love for God."

"It happened long ago," I reminded him.

"Time does not come into it," I was told. "Time is so short compared with Eternity; it is not allotted in equal slices to all living things on this earth."

"I don't know why we have to die. It's nice to be alive."

"Nobody wants to die but everybody wants to go to heaven."

"What is heaven?"

"Eternity. Seeing Almighty God, and from the beginning of time mankind has offered up sacrifices to His honour and glory. As time went on and the world's population grew and spread, sacrifices were offered to God in atonement for sin and in supplication, but the people became more displeasing to God, so much so that He destroyed the whole earth by flood, drowning every living thing except one good living man and his family and two of each species of fauna and feathers."

When I thought of all those dumb and innocent beautiful animals lying all over the world, dead rigid corpses, I was as mad as a wet hen myself.

"I don't like God very much," I told him.

My Lord chose not to hear that remark, but told me to look up at the sky.

I loved the sky with its countless dresses and changing faces; the vivid blue of spring with its trim of fleecy white clouds sailing across its surface, the dazzling glow of summer, hidden beneath a huge hat of cumulus vapour from time to time, or a scarf or two of cirrus with many tassels. The ominous deep dark cloak with a copper coloured collar heralding a tantrum of vicious lightning and oaths of thunder. Nothing more glorious have I ever beheld than an autumn sunset. The blood-red clouds edged with flaming gold drifting across the rose-coloured heavens like castles in the air. Winter skies shining through a lacework of leafless trees closer to heaven than mortals below them. All the clever dicks of this world can give sophisticated answers to this, but only God can make a tree.

A nudge and a quiet voice beside me said seriously, "Angel, I asked you to look up at the sky, not to actually go up there."

"It is so big," was all I could find to say.

"Space is vast," he agreed, "so endless that it cannot be measured in miles or minutes. It holds billions of stars, each one of which is a mysterious world of its own; there is more space, more stars and spheres called planets with their own moons, and farther away, still more space with no beginning and no end."

I could only repeat that it was so big, and after a short silence we came down to earth and back to the Old Testament.

"The world became adequately stocked with people again and they offered up their sacrifices to Almighty God, but as time went by, the sacrifices offered by them were no longer pleasing to their heavenly Father because they were becoming worse than even their forefathers before them."

My ears began to twitch in anticipation; I felt like that young girl whose name was Nellie. She had one foot on the straight and narrow path and the other hovered over the crooked and devious road leading down the hill, and comparing the one with the other, it seemed to me that the crooked path was the more attractive of the two. My teacher at school was very good with her Scripture, and she told us most interesting stories from the Old Testament, leaving out all the begatting and begotting bits and making her stories come alive. When she told us about Sara eavesdropping behind the flap of the tent when God was talking to Abraham, telling him that Sara was to have a baby, we could almost hear Sara laughing. After all, Sara was ninety years old and Abraham in his hundredth year! Many of us in school did not know our tables, but we were very well acquainted with the diabolical deeds of the leading characters of the Old Testament. Jealous brothers wanting to kill their dear brother, Joseph, but decided to throw him down into a pit, coat of many colours after him. Then he was hauled out by one or two of his kinder brothers who sold him to a band of Ishmaelites, and, after retrieving his coat of many colours and dipping it in the blood of a freshly killed kid, told their father that his beloved son was dead. In his anguish, perhaps Jacob spared a thought for Isaac, his own father, whom he had so callously deceived, and Esau, his brother whom he had robbed of his birthright blessing.

Then Isaac himself setting off to the land of vision where Abraham was to sacrifice him on an altar, Abraham carrying the knife and Isaac the wood for the holocaust on his shoulders.

My companion offered me a penny for my thoughts, so I told him about my views concerning sacrifice – the slaughter, the blood and the burning. I became profoundly sad and bowed my head; a habit of mine when I was on the verge of a heavy sulk, but my friend lightened up the atmosphere with a sensible bit of oratory. "Angel," he said gently, taking one of my hands into his, "whatever we think, whatever we do not understand, God loves the world."

"Then why does He let wars happen – why does He make wicked people who are cruel and going to hell to be roasted on a pitchfork, and not to heaven anyway?" I really wanted the answer most earnestly.

"Perhaps God turns evil into good. If one bad man or woman had ten children who were good and kind, is He going to spoil their chances of getting into heaven by not putting their fathers or mothers on this earth? And what is sin? What do you mean when you say 'wicked'?"

"Knitting on Sundays, playing 'Knocking down Ginger', flicking cigarette cards through somebody's letter box and knocking on the door and asking how far up the passage you flicked them – and once I drew a rude face on my teacher's front gate and smacked it."

"That must have given you a lot of satisfaction – drawing rude faces on your teacher's gate."

I shook my head reminiscently and said simply and without rancour, "No, she came out and caught me and gave me a clout round the ears and made me clean it off."

"Then why are you so cross with God for handing out holy clouts?"

"If we understood why He lets terrible things happen …"

"That is just the point, Angel. We do not understand God's reasons. If we did, we should be equal to God ourselves and everyone would be a little God."

"There are a lot of these little gods around now," I told him. "Sunday school teachers and vicars' daughters taking dripping round to the deserving poor …"

He cut my eloquence short by saying, "And little girls of the questing type carting bread and dripping around in paper bags. The only sacrifice acceptable to Almighty God is bread and wine."

"Why?"

"Because He sent His Son, Jesus Christ, to live amongst us and to teach us the way to salvation by offering up Himself on a wooden cross; the only sacrifice that could redeem the world. At the Last Supper, He taught His apostles to consecrate the bread and the wine into His body and blood. In that way, Jesus stays with us. He promised to be with us always until the end of the world. He also promised that the gates of hell would never prevail against His Church, and thanks to the many priests who came secretly to England using different names, disguising themselves as servants and labourers, offering Mass in hidden places, and bringing the Sacraments to the people, He is always with us."

"When did all this take place?"

"It began with King Henry VIII; he broke with the Church of Rome and became Head of the Church of England, and he wanted all his subjects to belong to his changed religion. When he died, his daughter, Mary, wanted the people to be Catholics again, so when her brother died and she became queen, she embarked on a campaign of cruelty against all those subjects who would not return to the Faith of their forefathers and burnt them to death as heretics."

"She was a wicked woman. My teacher said so."

"Child, perhaps we are not judged by what we do, but by our motives for doing wrong. Catholics were persecuted and imprisoned during the reign of Queen Elizabeth, but after the Gunpowder Plot to blow up King James and his Parliament the situation became even worse for the priests and their faithful followers. Many good people suffered torture and death so that the flame of faith in England would not be extinguished."

"I still don't understand why God let all this happen."

"To a little ant, all you appear to be is a couple of big black blobs which are the soles of your boots. He doesn't care what you actually are; all he knows is, he must get away pretty fast. Animals have no idea what we are doing when we sit with a book in our hands, reading; if they did, they would all be reading.

The thought of Oo-la-la sitting up straight on her cushion, pince-nez on nose, reading a copy of *The Times,* whilst Ichee-Koo sprawled under the table letting out a guffaw or two as he leaved through the pages of *Tit Bits* made me laugh so much that I slid off the stile. Then I noticed that two cows had been standing behind us listening to every word we said.

There is nothing more peaceful in this world than the face of a cow with its big beautiful sad-looking eyes. That is to say, when its mouth is shut. But one of these two had its mouth wide open as if with amazement.

My Lord turned his head and saw them and let out a bellow of amusement.

"Perhaps they can read after all," he chuckled, pointing to the 'Trespassers will be prosecuted' notice that was fixed on the other side of the stile behind the one on our side.

Shortly after our little discourse on the mysteries of faith, we said goodbye. Three things he told me – he said he was sure I was going to be more thoughtful towards my aunt Mary; he said he often sat on the fallen tree trunk in the grounds of Harvington when he said his Office and that he would be glad to see me; he looked down at my boots and said I was never to walk the three miles across to Harvington on a wet day. There was a hole in the upper part of one of my boots, and like the little girl who sat on Mother Kelley's doorstep, I had a hole in my sock where my toe peeped through.

My Lord stood there in the lane with the strong golden rays of the sun behind him, turning his silver hair to gold. Several times I turned and waved until distance dimmed his face and features, but not his outline against the sun. "Of course," I told myself, "he is God."

More often than not, My Lord would be sitting on his tree trunk saying his Office when I paid Harvington one of my frequent visits. Then I would crouch down on the grass beside him, my back resting against the tree trunk, my hands clasped about my knees, head bowed and chin on chest, waiting for him to get finished. Sometimes he said I reminded him of a hired mourner whilst at other times he said I put him in mind of Job when he found his sorrows too much for him.

There were times, too, when he looked desperately tired and his face was very pale, the usual gentle lines on it deeper, but his smile of greeting was always unchanged as was the warmth in his voice when he closed his breviary and bent forward to ruffle my hair.

Sometimes on his quiet tired days, we did not go into the house but spent an hour or two in the grounds in the shadow of the house amid the accompaniment of birdsong and sounds of croaking frogs, noisy grasshoppers and movements of very small life. He told me many things and above all else, he taught me many things which I stored away in the treasure-house of my mind. Things that throughout my lifetime would recur and guide me through the depths and walk with me when the sun was shining.

Sometimes My Dear would come out and join us. She would bring out a most beautifully packed lunch basket, and Bridie would lump and lurch behind her, almost hidden beneath a pile of rugs and cushions. There then would follow a most magnificent performance of devotion by maid making her mistress comfortable. On one of these occasions, when Bridie's head could be distinguished from the cushions she was hugging, I noticed for the first time what a handsome young woman she was. Her skin was pale, her hair was black, but her eyes were lovely in shape and colour; they were as blue as an autumn sky. My Lord saw me gawping at her and he bent and whispered in my ear, "Bridie has had a tuck put in her hair." And sure enough, she had had her hair 'bobbed'. Most women were having their hair cut and shedding hairpins all over the place.

Bridie saw the look of admiration on my face and gave me an exaggerated wink, but all she said was, "Begorra, an' the back o' hand to a young spalpane like yiz!"

Compliments were flying that day. I showed her the tip of my tongue and when My Lord turned his back to speak to his sister, she turned round and waved her left leg behind her as she made for the house.

"Vulgarity is very low," commented My Lord. "He must have eyes in the back of his head." I told myself, but aloud I told him very seriously, "Oh yes, vulgarity hangs very low – and you never know what's hanging till it drops!"

"I know that you are an incorrigible child," my friend told me as he moved along the trunk so that I could sit beside him.

It was pocket-lecture day, evidently, for as soon as we were settled to our satisfaction, he treated My Dear and me to a crash course on ugly gestures and the merits of avoiding them; he assured me that " the use of expletives was the prerogative of the ignorant …"

31

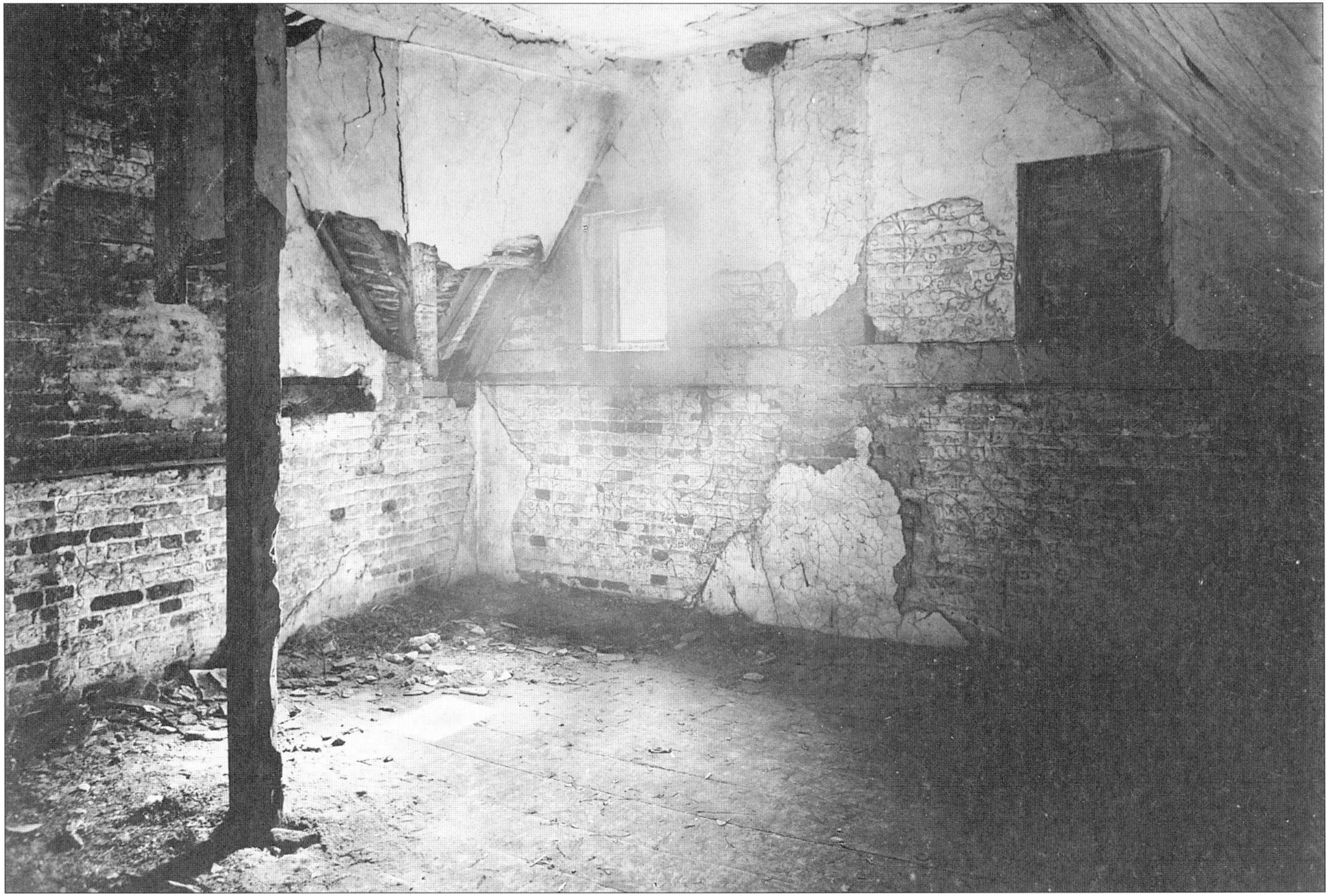

The Chapel

"He means bad language," interpreted his sister.

"… who are too unenlightened to express themselves in words," continued my friend, ignoring the interruption.

"Oh, you mean swearing," I told him.

"I mean that I wish you would not do it."

"I will never do it again," I solemnly swore.

After the briefest hesitation, My Dear raised her right hand and said, "I solemnly swear that I will never do it again."

Two pairs of eyes looked at her in astonishment. My Lord was absolutely lost for words, so I put in a few words of wisdom for him (courtesy of my aunt Mary).

"It just goes to show you," I pointed out, "that you should never judge the marmalade by the label on the pot!"

My Dear decided that a change of subject might be a good idea, so she told us that Bridie had fallen in love with the butcher.

"But she was in love with the postman three weeks ago," protested My Lord.

Feeling that it was time to add my little piece, I told them that my aunt Mary said that love was only a reconditioning of the reflexes.

"Your aunt Mary would do Old Moore's Almanac out of a job."

There followed one of those heavenly silences that I had grown to love dearly; my two friends wrapped in their own private thoughts while I sat idly watching the sunbeams glistening on the moat. Precious, tranquil moments albeit tinged with more than a hint of sadness, for although I was young, I knew instinctively that in all the years that would follow, nothing could ever compare with the sheer heaven of those days.

A cloud momentarily obscured the sun and the ancient house took on its air of sombre foreboding. I wriggled a bit closer to My Lord, who seemed to read my thoughts.

"Angel," he said very earnestly, "Harvington is a sad old house, much of its history has been lost in the march of time, many of its secrets will never come to light, but in spite of treachery, hatred and rigorous searching by pursuivants, no recusant was ever discovered in a secret hiding-place in Harvington Hall. Therefore, I firmly believe that Nicholas Owen contrived those hiding-places."

"Do some people say he didn't?"

"Not in so many words; they assume that the house did not come into the hands of Catholics until about 1630, long after 'Little John' Owen's death. But though little is known of the earlier Pakingtons, the ingenuity and endurance of those hidden places that were contrived in that house must be solely attributed to that master of builders, no matter when they were constructed."

My Lord looked up at the tall Tudor chimney stack in the low range of buildings as he went on talking.

"Flues were one of 'Little John's' specialities," he said, "because they were a means of supplying air and warmth to most of his hiding places."

"Let us talk about him for a short while," suggested My Dear, "then it will be time for lunch."

"I will start at the beginning. Nicholas Owen was a son of a staunch Catholic family who were established in Oxford. Two of his brothers were priests, whilst a third brother, Henry, followed the dangerous trade of Catholic printers. He once set up a secret press in the White Lion prison while he was detained there. It was possibly through Henry Owen, the printer, that Father Henry Garnet, S.J., first met Nicholas Owen, who, like himself, had served a term of imprisonment. Nicholas had been left lame due to an accident involving his horse, which may have been the reason why the Jesuits did not accept him into the Society as a priest. So he became a lay brother instead and servant to Father Garnet. He had much to say and did not mind saying it without lowering his voice – especially in his bold championship of Father Edmund Campion's innocence. His loud condemnation of the brutal treatment of priests was the reason for his first prison sentence. It seemed to be the only way to keep him quiet. After a time, however, his friends bought his release and his gaolers, believing that he had learnt his lesson, were glad to see him go. They said he was harmless anyway!

"It was not very long after he was set free that he played an important part with John Lillie and Richard Fulwood in assisting Father John Gerard, Jesuit, and John Arden, gentleman, to escape from the Tower of London. John Arden had been a prisoner in the Cradle Tower for ten years under the death sentence for his part in the Babington Plot. The Queen's Privy Garden separated these two prisoners, but they were able to communicate with each other by signs because John Arden was allowed to take exercise on the roof of the Cradle Tower and John Gerard was able to write messages in orange juice that became invisible until held in front of a fire. Also, John Arden's wife was allowed to visit her husband once or twice a week, and both men shared the same warder who permitted Father Gerard to visit John Arden's room. With the help of Mistress Arden and her large basket, everything for the celebrating of Mass was secretly and safely installed in her husband's prison room, and after ten long years John Arden received Holy Communion.

"During the days which followed, a plan of escape was devised by the two prisoners. Father Gerard had noticed how close the Cradle Tower was to the moat which surrounded the outer fortifications and convinced his friend that it would not be difficult to attach a rope from the roof of the tower and have a friend fix it to a stake by the wall beyond the moat. John Arden thought the idea was worth trying, but he pointed out that loyal friends would be needed. Father Gerard replied, 'We have the friends all right.'

"The plan, after a second attempt, proved successful, and after getting down the rope and embarking in a rowing boat, they landed at a spot where Nicholas Owen was waiting for them with horses.

"For seventeen years 'Little John' Owen worked as Father Garnet's servant and he constructed hiding-places for priests in the great houses of recusant families. So Harvington, ringed by several mansions and owned by the Catholic branch of the Pakingtons, must have had those many hiding-places contrived by none other than Nicholas Owen.

"Father Garnet applied to Claudius Aquaviva, who was General of the Society of Jesus, to recognise the devoted services of 'Little John' (and others) by bestowing on them the title of 'Lay Brother'.

"Nicholas Owen was starved out of one of his own hiding-places at Hindlip Hall (it was known then as Hindlip House) together with Ralph Ashley. They had hidden Father Garnet and Father Oldcorne in another hiding-place in the house with sufficient provisions to last for several days. Owen and Ashley tried to pass themselves off as servants but they were arrested by Sir Henry Bromley, Sheriff of Worcestershire. A day or two afterwards, the two priests were caught when one of the searchers discovered their hiding-place.

"Three of the captives paid with their lives, but Nicholas Owen died under torture in the Tower. At the king's request, Father Garnet was allowed to hang until he was dead, and when his head was held up by the executioner, who called out 'God save the King!', none of the spectators answered the customary 'Amen'. Some of them set upon the executioner and came within a hair's breadth of killing him, while the rest departed in tears."

My Lord bowed his head. It seemed as if those few moments had been taken from Eternity. Time had ceased to exist; the years and years that had passed since 1606 seemed not to have existed. The many who had died for their faith seemed to pass in slow procession before my eyes. All those 'Johns' – the much-loved and admired Robert Southwell, Edmund Campion, Henry Garnet and all the rest of them. And above all, the humble servants of those magnificent priests – Nicholas Owen, John Lillie and Ralph Ashley.

Time returned. The phantoms faded into the haze beyond the trees. My Dear was carefully folding her knitting.

Bridie came out of the house all dressed up like nobody's business. It was her half day and she was going to the pictures to see Mary Pickford in a film entitled 'Human Sparrows', and for the occasion she was wearing her best hat, which was a glorious affair – straw with a very wide brim and lavishly trimmed with cherries and green ribbon – how the ladies in the church must have loved it! It puzzled me why she wore it to go the pictures because nobody was going to see it in the dark.

"Wheeee!" exclaimed My Lord, looking at Bridie. "Hush!" said My Dear, looking at him.

Then two pairs of eyes were focussed on me as their owners awaited my comments on the subjects of hats and headgear but as I had never to my knowledge ever possessed one, there was little I could say, so I merely remarked, "If you can't fight, do wear a big hat!"

My Lord stood up and walked towards the house to wash his hands while his sister proceeded to spread the cloth and put out the places and cutlery with me checking anxiously to see whether she was putting out two plates or three. In case you think for one minute that I was a mercenary urchin, I would like to explain that I was motivated by economical influences. If I was not to be invited for lunch, nothing would make me go into the house and wash my hands. No indeed!

My Dear paused in her preparations and regarded me very thoughtfully. She wore a very puzzled expression on her face, an expression I had often noticed when she looked at me. Then she suddenly said very slowly, "You are a strange little girl. You are like that old house that you love so dearly – full of hidden places and thoughts and desires like the corridors and passages branching off at all angles."

Since I did not understand what she was talking about, I made no answer, and she went on, "You are a great consolation to my brother in many ways. He feels that the flame of faith must grow brighter and that Harvington should become a shrine to all the martyrs who never betrayed nor disowned Jesus Christ. He firmly believes that prayer is so powerful and with God all things are possible, but he is nearing the end of his quest for an answer to his prayers, but I believe that he somehow knows that you with your devotion and tenacity will continue this quest. I think he is right."

Everything she said was beyond my reasoning, and feeling sure it was 'nice' talk, I felt cherished and very happy. To be honest, though, I have to say the happiness attained its full measure when I saw that My Dear had put three plates on the table.

The Nursery

Chapter 4

Roofs and Chimneys

AFTER TWO days of intermittent rain, the sun shone down on a shining fresh green world of Harvington. I was sitting on the parapet of the east bridge, my legs hanging over the water of the moat, my head stretched back as far as it would go, turned towards the house, or rather, to the roof of the house. I had just seen the tail end of My Lord disappearing behind a chimney stack – the tall one sticking up like a nose in the middle of the low wing of the house. I had no idea what he was going up there, but, after all, as I had always believed, he was God, so I naturally concluded that he was making his way down from heaven.

Cupping my hands round my mouth, I bawled out, "Oi!" loud enough to waken the dead.

Bridie shot through the main gateway with a homicidal expression on her face. "Yiz be after holdin' hiz whist!" she shrieked out, bawling me considerably, "By all the holy harps in heaven, I'll be after clatting yiz face for yiz!"

To my mind came one of my aunt Mary's wise quotations, 'Never insult a mother alligator until you have crossed the river (Haitian proverb)." I hastily swung my feet back over the parapet on to terra firma, having no desire to be pushed into the moat.

My Lord suddenly appeared, and his silver hair had been blown by the wind into an upstanding halo round his head.

"So nice to see you bosom friends making daisy chains together," he remarked, to which Bridie made no answer, but turned her back and stalked towards the house.

"What were you doing on the roof?" I wanted to know.

"Oh, I was just doing this and that and practising my Santa Claus act ready for Christmas."

"No you weren't. You were looking for something. What was is?"

"Curiosity killed the cat."

He had a point there. Curiosity had come close to finishing me off on more than one occasion, before My Lord had firmly stressed that I must never go exploring in that old house alone ever again. On one of these little tours I came within a few inches of ending up a dead rigid corpse on the courtyard below. It happened on a very dull afternoon when the sun seemed to have taken the day off. There was a dank chilly atmosphere pervading the entire house and the deep shadows in remote corners came creeping forward,

The North side

bringing their smaller relations with them. Over all hung an invisible curtain of deep melancholy, loneliness and an eeriness that seeped into my bones.

Groping my way up to the attic landing, I was confronted by a selection of doors that didn't seem to know what they were doing there, because they either wouldn't open at all or the rooms beyond them were like cupboards. The only door that I was interested in was situated at the end of a short passage. That door was firmly fastened on the other side. I had made several unsuccessful attempts to open that door, and there being a tantalising feeling of frustration assailing my ego, I decided to find out what exactly lay beyond that locked, barred or bolted door. On that afternoon I soon found out.

Since my previous visit to the door, a large lump of masonry had fallen from a nearby wall and lay in a heap of rubble on the passage floor close to the mysterious door. Failing to see it in the gloom, I stumbled and fell headlong, banging my head full blast against the lower half of the door. Either my head was as hard as a bullet or the bottom part of the door was rotten, for with a hideous wood shriek, most of the door fell outwards, almost taking me with it. As it was, one of my arms and my head was hanging over space and I was just in time to see a big piece of door hanging crazily on the top of the ivy before it fell down about fifty feet to the stones below.

For a few moments I lay stunned and then, when the world had steadied itself, I slowly, by using my toes, inched my way backwards until I was able to pull my arm, that was hanging over space, back inside. So, with the aid of two hands and two feet, my progress became quicker until, at last, I was able to turn myself right side up and sit by the pile of rubble gazing up at the huge hole up on the wall speculatively, wondering what was in that hole or where it led. I would have climbed up to investigate, but I had nothing to stand on and, by this time, there was a lump as big as an egg on the top of my head, and the Weymouth Chimes were ringing loud and clear inside my brain. There was also another inconvenience; I was very giddy when I tried to get to my feet, so I sat down again and had a little nap. It was quite dark when I eventually groped my way out of the house and pointed my nose towards home, but I didn't get there until the next day, when a farmer discovered me asleep underneath a cow, and as there was a big tree close by, it was presumed that I had tried to climb it and had fallen out. I was glad to let them go on presuming, but my aunt Mary knew me too well; she often said that I was more at home up a tree and what a pity it was I hadn't a tail. So, after a night of desperate anxiety, all she did was to give me one of her 'looks' which would have pulverised a consolidated nonchalant jellied eel.

My Lord was treating me to one of his quizzical looks, obviously waiting for me to five him an edifying account of my thoughts, but all I was able to say was, "How did you get up there on the roof?"

This was not a moment for banter. He told me the simple facts. "I climbed through a hole high up on a wall, and there was a secret kind of little door hanging open and leading to a walkway right up in the roof. In parts, there are floor boards rotting away and only the joists left. The whole place is wide but low so you can only crawl along, and not high enough to let you turn round to go back the way you came."

"So how did you get on the roof?"

"I crawled along and came to a tiny little room hidden in a gable of the roof. Most of the floor of this little place had disappeared, so that I was able to see down into the room below, so I climbed down and found myself in the chapel next to Lady Mary's Nursery."

Sidling up to him and getting as close to him as I could possibly get, I measured myself against him. My head did not quite reach his elbow. He was well up to standard that morning.

"Don't you dare," he said very sternly, reading my thoughts, "go up there. Not ever. Besides, you have already given me a promise never to go into that house alone."

"Of course, there must be a more convenient way to reach that room over the chapel," My Lord was saying reflectively, as if he was talking to himself, "and I think some of those chimney stacks and flues and shafts are not as innocent as they look, standing up there pointing up to heaven."

He gave me his one-eyebrow-raised grin, "Wouldn't you agree, Angel?"

My mind's eye conjured up a vision of recusants scrambling over the roofs and the pursuivants careering along after them.

"Fancy having to climb up walls to get in and out of a room at the top of a house."

"Flues have more uses than one. Hides built near flues could be warm and supplied with air. A search could last for days or weeks and even months."

"You still have not told me how you got on the roof?"

He stood looking me over from feet to apex, much as if I were an exhibit in an antique shop window. He was making a profound decision. Then at last he said, "Very well, I will show you and I only hope I know what I am doing. But remember your promise never to go into the house alone. Never to go searching for secret places by yourself. If official searchers could not fine them, a little girl would never stand a chance of discovering them."

There was a room on the first floor known as 'The South Room', and on the left side of the fireplace was a scullery with a sink in it. It was once a garderobe that drained into the moat. My Lord pointed out as he bent and raised the floorboards that came up in one piece because there was another layer of wood nailed on the underside of it and the whole arrangement was so heavy that My Lord was puffing like a dragon when he up-ended it against the wall.

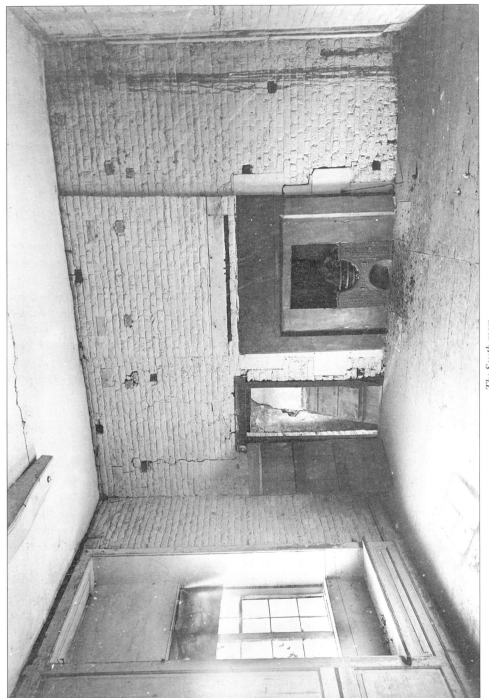

The South room

Peering down, we saw, in the light of My Lord's torch, a small chamber with an earth floor, about six feet below. My friend swung himself over the edge of the hole in great style, but my performance was less noteworthy as he raised his hands and lifted me down. You could see nothing exciting to start with, but my friend pointed to a large hole about eighteen inches square near the bottom of the wall and hidden from above by the floor joists. It was just big enough for a slim person to squeeze through. We did not crawl through that hole, although I was willing enough. So we took turns to look through it and marvel at the sheer ingenuity of the hide built in a shaft that went right up to the roof among the chimneys. My Lord shone his torch down into the lower part of the shaft, but all we were able to see was a huge mound of rubble where a large portion of the wall had collapsed. The outside wall was intact, the wall that must have been constructed to conceal the shaft from the outside view.

"It is supposed that underneath all that debris is a secret way to an underground tunnel," my friend explained as he shone his light towards the top of the shaft again. Actually, there was a feeble glimmer of light filtering down the shaft, so I declined his offer of the torch when my turn came to poke my head through the hole, and what I saw was a very large pulley wheel right up in the roof and near enough for me to touch it in the shaft was a smaller wheel that formed a pulley to guide a rope over the big wheel above. I saw, too, that there was a very small door in the shaft quite close to the large wheel.

I drew my head inside and looked up into his face. "There is a way up to the roof up that shaft. You – you did not go up that way?"

"Not on your sweet young life," he assured me. "Anyway, there is no rope. It is probably lying underneath all the bricks and masonry at the bottom of the shaft."

"Aren't you ever going to tell me how you got on the roof?"

"We get out of here first before we suffocate. This is too small a room to accommodate one person in comfort, much less two."

I most certainly saw the point, and when I pondered over his reason for bringing me down to see the pulley hide high up in the roof, it dawned on me that he was trying to divert my mind from the burning desire to know how he had got onto the roof.

Getting out of the tiny room was a work of art. My Lord simply put his hands underneath my elbows and lifted me up until my head and arms arrived back in the South Room, and whilst I hung on to the edge of the hole, he grabbed my feet and gave a mighty shove, sending the rest of me to join the top part of me in the scullery doorway. He, of course, swung himself up with the greatest of ease – Tarzan could not have done better! For his age, he was extremely strong and very agile. Of course he was God.

When he had replaced the scullery floor and after we had dusted ourselves down, although I feel bound to say, he was more pernickety about spiders and their webs than I was, I ventured to mention the roof again.

He let out a hard-driven sigh. "Angel with a dirty face," he said very seriously, "why don't you go and join the suffragettes?!"

"Why?"

"It would give you something else to think about and stop you mewing about the roof."

"Well, I love roofs. I have always adored roofs. I would be so happy if I could go on a roof."

He gave a handsome mock bow. "And I know why you want to sit on a rooftop."

"Because I haven't got a broomstick?"

"No. Because a rooftop is as near to heaven as you will ever get unless you stop whingeing to get your own way."

We were still on the first floor and we turned into a little room he called 'Dr. Dodd's Library', and in answer to my "Who was he?", My Lord told me that Charles Dodd, whose real name was Hugh Tootell, had been a priest at Harvington for seventeen years. He had written a church history in this small room. He may have been a very difficult teacher to live with, but nobody could ever doubt the deep sincerity of his love for Harvington and its history.

"When did he live here?"

"About two hundred years ago, give or take a few years."

Doctor Dodd's Library conjured up feelings of profound interest within me. There was the room itself with its brickwork underwear and solid wooden uprights, standing empty and so forlorn where once a man had sat, quill in hand working steadily at his labour of love. His work was supposedly printed in Brussels but was actually printed in Wolverhampton, and paid for by the Duke of Norfolk.

My Lord pointed out a wide ledge that ran right across one end of the room which was about five foot high. "That used to be a book cupboard but the doors disappeared long ago." Then he indicated a very heavy-looking oak beam in the right wall of the recess. "When you press on the top of that upright, the bottom swings outwards leaving a space just large enough for a man to squeeze through."

"And you have climbed up on that shelf and been through the hole?"

"Yes, there is a small room behind that gap in the wall about three feet wide, three yards long and not high enough for me to stand upright in."

"So you had to crawl."

"Yes, my astute young friend, I had to crawl. I could even say that I have done more crawling in this house than I have ever done before."

"Where did you crawl to? How did you get out? What did you find in there?"

Dr. Dodd's Library

"First I found a bolt behind the pivot that works the swinging beam so that a fugitive could lock himself in –"

"Or herself –"

Choosing to ignore my pushy remark, he continued, "And on the left hand wall there is a hole – it might once have been a door – it leads through the back of a fixed cupboard on the landing near the chapel. One of those rooms has an escape route through a false fireplace and up a shaft among the chimney stacks on the roof."

"And that is how you got on the roof."

"Amen."

When he said "Amen" it meant that the subject was closed, so I turned my thoughts back to Doctor Charles Dodd. I pictured him sitting at his desk or table in front of his window, the rays of sun shining on his pink bald head, quill in hand moving swiftly over page after page on the pleasant days of inspiration and the dry days when the fountains of thought would not turn on, and his hand moved slowly with many a pause across a page.

The ivy and creepers outside the window made the room very dim in a greeny kind of way and my imagination had reached such a pitch that I could almost see him sitting there with his head bent over his work. I could almost hear the scratching of his quill as I stood there letting my imagination run riot, and it was then that a great desire was born either in my head or my heart – I was not clever enough to sort it out – I wanted a pen and some ink and a stack of exercise books about fourteen feet high. I wanted to write – I wanted to put words down on paper.

The question was, what words?

The South side

46

Chapter 5

Desolation

CAME THE DAY when it all ended like the closing of a book. It began as usual with the sun beaming down on fresh green meadows and gleaming streams. The birds' songs seemed muted and there was a hint of autumn in the air accompanied by a sense of foreboding. In some inexplicable way, the day was different as I made my way towards Harvington. It was indeed a different kind of day, for instead of finding him at Harvington, My Lord had come to meet me; I found him sitting on the 'Trespassers-will-be-prosecuted' stile, and the very sight of him banished all my feelings of gloom, whilst the warmth and happiness that always filled my heart and spirit at the sight of him swept over me like the tide sweeps over a beach.

"Good morning, my little off-white angel."

There was something different about the way he said the 'my' bit in his greeting. Gone was the teasing tone of his voice and no raising of an eyebrow, but I was far too young to understand the extraordinary wealth of meaning he put into that barely audible 'my'.

The moment of sadness passed in a flash and I heaved myself up on the stile beside him in anticipation of a glorious few hours of his company.

He understood my thoughts.

"We will have a very good day," he promised. "My sister and Bridie have gone to town on a shopping spree and will not be back until after tea."

"Is Bridie taking all the angels and saints with them?"

"I don't think the angels and saints go on shopping trips. Can you imagine the angels ever wearing hats instead of haloes?"

"No. And they would have to carry handbags instead of harps, wouldn't they?"

"There are the saints, of course. They might be able to go in for new hats but I don't think they would come down here to buy them."

"Are there lots of ladies up there in heaven?" I asked.

"I have not been up there to count them, but have you any particular lady in mind?"

"My Aunt Mary said there were two sisters, Eleanor and Anne, sisters of Guy Fawkes."

He gave a hearty laugh. "No, they were not related to Guy. The sisters were the daughters of Lord Vaux, which name sounds very like Fawkes. Guy Fawkes had a stepfather, Dennis Bainbridge, who was a devout Catholic and Guy himself joined the Catholic faith although he understood how much the Catholics were made to suffer."

"I know all about him," I replied, "but my Aunt Mary reckons the Gunpowder Plot was all a put-up job to stir more hatred up against the Catholics – and the men who were hunting them down and collecting bounty and stealing their possessions were beginning to get worried in case the King was getting more lenient towards recusants."

"It could also have been one devilish plot to get Father Henry Garnet, who was the Superior of the Jesuit mission in England. His enemies arrested him as the instigator of the Gunpowder Plot and hanged him without having a single shred of evidence against him. Father Oldcorne was hanged because he was caught in the same priest-hole at Hindlip as Father Garnet. They were in hiding for eight days."

"I would like to hear about Lord Vaux's daughters."

"Two very brave ladies. Eleanor Brooksby was the eldest of Lord Vaux's three daughters and was Father Garnet's hostess at Shoby in Leicestershire, and her sister, Anne, shared the house with her because after three years of marriage, Eleanor was left a widow with two children, William and Mary."

"What happened to the middle sister?"

"Elizabeth joined the Poor Clares in Rouen."

"What is a Poor Clare?"

"An order of nuns who follow the rule of St. Clare, who was a friend of Francis of Assisi. Anne Vaux followed her vocation in her constant care for Father Garnet."

"How?"

"She had influential friends among the leading recusant families in high places. Her brother and two sisters lost their mother when Anne was a month old."

"What happened to the four children?"

"Their father took another wife. She was Mary Tresham; her father, John Tresham, had married Eleanor Catesby, daughter of Anthony Catesby, but both Mary's parents died on the same day, and her wardship had been bought by Sir Robert Throckmorton of Coughton. So, through marriage, the two Vaux sisters were connected to the families of Catesby, Tresham and Throckmorton. Through these two sisters with their financial aid and help from their relatives, Father Garnet was able to set up a network of great houses all over England where priests could be sheltered in order to prevent the flame of faith burning out in England."

"What about the brother?"

"Henry was a very devout man. He gave up his claim to the title in order to serve God in his own humble way. He was imprisoned for his faith and died soon after he was released from the Marshalsea prison."

"They were all very brave."

"There was one very brave girl, Frances Burroughs, only eleven years old.

She was the daughter of Maud Burroughs, Eleanor's aunt, who had recently died leaving a large family, so Eleanor had immediately adopted Frances to bring her up as her own daughter."

"How was she so brave? What did she do?"

"She was never daunted and never feared anything. Father Garnet and another priest were at Mass when a search party arrived at the house, but Frances foiled them. These searchers were determined to find Father Garnet; they had already searched Lord Vaux's house in Hackney for Father Southwell, but he had given them the slip."

"How?"

"Simply by walking faster than his would-be trackers. So the party of searchers took up the search at Shoby, hoping to capture either Father Southwell or Father Garnet, or, better still, both of them. But they had not reckoned on an eleven-year-old child throwing a spanner in the works, or to put it more elegantly, the hand of Divine Providence working through a courageous little girl."

"How?"

"When Anne and Eleanor heard the commotion below, they went downstairs to confront the searchers, taking young Frances with them, who stood at the foot of the stairs glaring at the pursuivants who were waiting with drawn swords.

"The undismayed Frances said, 'Put up your swords! Or else my mother will die; she cannot bear to see a naked blade!' Then making as if to fetch some wine for Eleanor, she ran back upstairs and made fast the doors of the hiding place where the priests were safely hidden."

"Wheeee!"

"On another occasion, soon after that, she barred the staircase after a sudden intrusion of pursuivants. Just to frighten her, one of them drew his dagger and held it at her breast, threatening to stab her if she did not hand over the hidden priests. With great composure, Frances retorted, "If thou dost, it will be the hottest blood that ever thou sheddedst in thy life." And she was only eleven years old. Only a year older than you, Angel."

I looked at him and took in every detail; the silky white hair, the face kind of seamed with the living of many years, belied by the steady youthful glance from his grey eyes. I knew than as I know now, that I would have died any death for him.

"Oh, Frances, Frances, if ever I reach that wonderful place beyond the reach of time, I hope we meet surrounded by all those wonderful souls who laboured for Jesus Christ on earth and abide with Him in heaven."

All I could find to say was, "What became of Frances?"

"She joined the Ursuline nuns, an order founded by Saint Angela Merici."

"Do you think I will ever be a nun?"

"You have to have a vocation: that means a call from God."

"Do you think I will ever get one of those vocations?"

He put his head on one side in order to study me very carefully and, after much consideration, he slowly shook his head.

"At this moment, my Angel, I don't think it at all likely."

The things that My Lord knew! But of course he was God! He was also hungry and so was I (of course), but we did pause for a short while as we crossed the bridge on our way into the house to raid the larder, to inspect a hole in the east wall just above the water of the moat.

"I'd like to know what that hole is," I told him.

"That's easy," he replied, "it was the escape door from the shaft where the pulley hide was. The shadow of the bridge made the shadows on the water so dark that a fugitive could silently swim across the moat without being detected even if there was a guard on duty on the bridge."

I remembered the time when we looked through the hole in the wall of the hiding place under the floor of the scullery of the room on the first floor. All we had seen below us was a pile of rubble where part of the inner wall had fallen in, blocking the bottom part of the shaft entirely.

We had a splendid lunch. My Lord settled for a piece of cold pie with a considerable amount of greenery livened up with bright splashes of tomato and long thick whiskers of pickled cabbage, whilst I did more than justice to a slab of boiled bacon sardines and a great splosh of OK sauce. He washed His food down with a glass of beer and I politely accepted a glass of lemonade poured from a glass bottle with a pressed-in bit near the top and a glass marble chasing from side to side as the drink was poured. Had I been given a choice, I most certainly would have gone in for the beer. Still, you cannot have everything in this world, and anyway, I did not have to wash my hands, and, now I come to think of it, neither did he.

We spent the afternoon in the Hall, going from room to room, observing all the special details of every mysterious passage, seeming to lead nowhere; the great void where once a magnificent staircase had stood; the empty echoes caused by our boots on floors; room after room with its own individual atmosphere of history, adventure and endurance, all bound up together in an overall feeling of sadness and supplication. To me, it was a house with a soul, begging not to be left to crumble away into the dust; a house that had not yet fulfilled its purpose.

My Lord's thoughts must have been travelling in the same train as mine (only in a First Class compartment), for he said thoughtfully, "This house should become a shrine; its walls have given shelter to many a soul prepared to shed his blood for the Catholic cause."

"Nobody was caught here, you said."

"Nobody that we know about, certainly, because the hiding-places were too

The Withdrawing Room

well constructed to be discovered, and I daresay there are more secret places in this house that will never be found. So much of the history of Harvington is as secret as its mysterious undiscovered hidden places."

I understood every word he said; I was only ten, but the atmosphere of deep melancholy that pervaded every room, together with the wind singing through the secluding trees outside, and singing in the rafters above the attics, mingling with the air I was breathing, becoming so dear, so meaningful, so spellbinding as to render me speechless.

On our way down to pay our respects to Father Wall's secret little room (as I called it), we passed the passage where a door dividing me from Eternity had once stood.

My Lord stood eyeing the space reflectively, while I silently regarded him with more than a little apprehension.

"Extraordinary," he muttered. "That door, if it had simply rotted away, would have fallen inwards; the lintels on the outside are very sturdy still and are strongly in place, so I can't help thinking that that door was probably kicked down."

Unconsciously, I put up a hand and touched the scar on my head. Though it was hidden by my hair; it was still very sore.

Nothing missed his keen eye, and it came as no surprise when be bent towards me and placed a hand on my head and when his fingers came into contact with my skull, he let out a long low whistle.

"It's only ringworm," I tried to assure him, but he was not accepting that; I should have understood by then that he did not agree that a clean lie was better than a dirty piece of truth. In fact, he was angry, or so I thought.

"Child," he said sternly, "I want Judgement Day truth from you, so tell me what happened to your head!"

So I explained briefly but explicitly. "Before you came, I tried to open the door, but it wouldn't open, and then I fell and hit it with my head and the bottom half fell off."

My Lord was quiet for so long that I thought he had forgotten about me, but at last he said, "I have written a letter to your Auntie Mary. See that you do not go home without it."

I didn't exactly wonder what he had written in that letter; I thought it was a note to remind her that she had not said her prayers lately. After all, he was God, and we made our way to Father Wall's little hidden room, as we always did when we went into the house; not to go down into the little place, but to kneel at the foot of the stairs and say our prayers. This afternoon, though, it was different, for instead of putting his hands together as he usually did, he covered his face with them and bowed his head very low.

We stayed much longer than we usually did, and when we at last got on to our feet, it seemed that he had just returned from a distant world. Naturally,

I understood (or thought I did) so I was silent as we walked through the Great Chamber, peeped into Doctor Dodd's Library, where I waved and blew a kiss towards the place where I imagined he might have sat, admired afresh the small panelled room that had been Lady Mary Yate's bedroom with its beautiful overmantel; a room that must have been a haven for her during the unquiet years of persecution, her father and his friend, Thomas Habington of Hindlip Hall, under house arrest being listed in London as recusants, the many times her home must have been raised by pursuivants tearing the place apart. The tranquillity of this dignified room must have afforded deep consolation in her darkest hours when death called away so many beloved members of her family and friends.

We were very tired when at last we left the house, because we had lingered in its lonely rooms for a long time. If only their walls could have uttered words, what tales they could have told.

My Dear and Bridie had returned from their spree by this time and were busy preparing a high-class tea in the kitchen. At Aunt Mary's we seldom had a knife-and-fork dinner, but a knife-and-fork tea was something you went to bed and had dreams about. To the heavenly smell of frying bacon, I assisted Bridie to set the table whilst My Lord hacked slices of bread from a gorgeous crusty loaf.

Bridie seemed to have a bad cold; her eyes were pink round the rims and her nose looked swollen, while every now and then, least when expected, she gave a tremendous sniff.

"Sure an' me appetite is gone," she wailed when she was asked how many rashers she would like to have put on her place, "I'll just be after taking a small tea. Three rashers, two eggs, and I'll try to be eating two slices of fried bread, but I cannot be eating much, you understand –"

"My Aunt Mary says," I told them seriously, though I was more than happy with the contents of my plate, "that our body is the temple of the Holy Spirit, and therefore we should be careful about what we put in our stomach."

Bridie let out a snort that must have reverberated up, down and round the Malvern Hills.

My Lord said simply, "Our Lord said it was not what a man putteth into his stomach, but that what cometh out of his heart that matters."

My Dear looked carefully at her brother, their maid and the little hanger-on so busily champing away.

"And those who speaketh with their mouths full are likely to choketh."

Bridie, apart from the odd sniff or two, became very quiet, so was My Lord who wore an expression of deep thoughtfulness, whilst My Dear, ever serene, replenished empty plates. I ate!

Soon after tea, it was time for me to go home. My Lord was to accompany me as usual for part of the way according to his usual custom, but My Dear acted quite out of character by giving me a kiss and a hug that lasted longer than any cuddle I could ever remember being given in all my life, and I felt so warm and cherished that I did not know what to do with myself. So I stood there saying nothing at all until Bridie chimed in with her little piece. She gave me a bear-like embrace, a little blue rosary and a large piece of her mind.

"Yiz are a greedy, gormandizing, disgusting, disgraceful, good-for-nothing young varmint, and 'tis certain sure the devil will be after getting you with his pitchfork –"

"And good evening to you," I told her cheekily. Talk about the pot calling the kettle black!

"And I'll be after praying for yiz to all the glorious saints on high, and I'll offer up all the sufferings of me poor bleeding heart –"

My Lord cut short her litany by almost hustling me off the premises.

We had little to say to each other as we walked along side by side. Perhaps all had been said in that fragment of time that we had known each other. The happiness I had known in the hours spent in his company was beyond all description; too precious to explain in words.

He seemed to be reluctant to turn and go back towards Harvington; in fact, we were almost in sight of the cottage when he held out a bag he had been carrying. "My sister sent these few things for your Aunt Mary," he explained, "and I have put a letter inside the bag for your Aunt."

I looked at him searchingly; something was different and the grave look on his face warned me that 'different' was hardly the word.

He bent and rested his hands upon my shoulders and looked into my face for a while as if he was trying to find the right words to say. Then the words came at last.

"My little off-white Angel," he said gently, "this is where we have to say goodbye."

This cold hand seemed to clutch at my heart; I felt the ice forming and settling round all my senses so that I could not speak, could see nothing but his face with its kind eyes, until I could bear it no longer and bowed my head.

"You see, little one," he explained in a voice so quiet that I could hardly hear his words, "my day's work is nearly done, and soon I must pass through that gate that divides Time and Eternity. You will go on loving Harvington and pray that one day it will become a shrine to the memory of all who suffered and died so that the light of faith in England would never burn out."

Never in the many years that were destined to make up my lifetime was I to ache as I was aching them; my heart had no tears to give. I opened my mouth to speak, but no words would come out of it.

My Lord bent and kissed the top of my head.

"Goodbye."

Blindly I turned and moved towards home, head bowed, seeing nothing, not even stopping to look back. Habit was the guide that steered my feet along that last lap of the journey home, for I could not remember it. All I was able to recollect was Aunt Mary in her little front garden murdering the weeds.

She looked up as I passed her. "How nice to see you," she said sarcastically, but looking at me more closely, she changed her tone. "What's the matter? Lost sixpence and found a penny?"

Making no reply, I went straight into the house, flung the bag I had been carrying onto the table and went and sat on the kitchen doorstep with my hands clasped round my knees, my chin pressed against my chest until the anguish abated and the desolation moved in.

My Aunt Mary, with the wisdom of Solomon, left me along with my grief. She was very pleased with the contents of the bag, anyway. In it was a beautiful black shawl for herself and two pairs of stockings for me, which I had seen My Dear knitting. For Ichee-Koo there was a new collar, and Oo-La-La got enough satin ribbon to hang herself. But it was the letter from My Lord that charmed her most. She tipped out of the envelope quite a lot of money, but it was the letter that put the misty look in her eyes.

I asked her next morning what was written in the letter, hoping that she would let me read it. She refused to part with it and carefully transferred it from the table to her 'holy' pocket, a place where she kept her small treasures. There was plenty of room for the letter.

"It says in the letter that I am to take you into the town and buy you a new pair of boots."

"Is that all?"

She made no reply but busied herself making tea, and when she pushed my mug towards me, I wrapped my hands round it, in a futile effort to seek comfort in its warmth, but when I tried to drink some of the tea, it would not go past the lump in my throat.

Before we set off to buy the new boots, my Aunt Mary made me put on a pair of my new stockings and she herself attended to my ablutions by smacking a wet flannel round my face and drying it on a towel that could have done with a bit of soap and water itself.

We approached what was in those days known as the 'bottle and jug' part of the town; that meant the poorer district where things were slightly cheaper. I automatically stopped outside the 'in and out shop'.

Most of these establishments were pawn-shops with three great big brass balls hanging above a window displaying unredeemed pledges, mostly watches and jewellery and a knick-knack or two off the parlour whatnot. Some of these shops had lines of new boots hanging like huge bunches of black bananas outside a wide open door where lines of clothes hung in bright profusion, or chaotic confusion (according to a person's viewpoint), where you went in one side to take what you needed to buy and, when your choice was made, you went out the other side.

"Come on," said Aunt Mary, "we are not going in there."

"But we always go in there."

"Not today, we're not," she told me firmly.

So, to my great astonishment, she walked us briskly to the classy part of the town and we did not stop until we reached the most high-class boot shop in existence. We went in. Aunt Mary had every pair of boots out of its box and although I was too low in spirit myself to care, I couldn't help noticing that the shop assistant was looking very tired and exceedingly jaded by the time we left the shop with the most handsome pair of boots I had ever had in my life. Out of all that money My Lord had sent her, there was only fourpence left, so she bought a pair of kippers for our tea.

All the way home I hugged the box containing my beautiful boots. The lady in the shop suggested I wore them to go home in, but I was having none of that. I refused to insult my lovely boots by putting them on to come into contact with dirty paving stones.

Whilst Aunt Mary cooked the kippers, I laid the table for tea, taking care to choose a newspaper tablecloth that she had read, otherwise she would have given me a full recital of her vast vocabulary. She and Bridie made a good verbal pair, but whereas Bridie called on all the saints in heaven, this aunt of mine evoked the aid of all the devils in hell. She was absolutely wonderful; she could go on without stopping for half an hour, never using the same word twice! It was a performance I thoroughly enjoyed on ordinary days, but this was not an ordinary day; it was a day of heartbreak, and I wanted quiet in my unhappiness.

When Aunt Mary put a kipper in front of me, totted up nicely with a big knob of margarine, I made an effort to swallow some of it, but the lump in my throat became unbearably painful. I pushed my plate away and, leaving the table, sat myself on the kitchen doorstep until bedtime.

The sun continued to shine; birds kept themselves busy while the leaves of the trees took out their dresses of red and gold, but I saw nothing of the beauties of the approaching autumn.

I must have driven Aunt Mary almost out of her mind, for I refused to have my hair washed, I would not wear my new boots – I took the box containing them to bed with me every night. I absolutely refused to go to school. Nature compelled me to eat, but it had now become a chore instead of a highlight of existence.

They were not the days for taking recalcitrant children to the Child Guidance people and so my aunt took me to see a doctor. He was a kind sort of man, and he asked me some questions, then he diagnosed my case as 'nervous debility' and opening a cabinet he took out a large bottle of venomous-looking medicine and handed it to my Aunt Mary with instructions that I was to take one tablespoon three times a day. I glowered at the bottle in my aunt's hand; I glowered at the doctor, but I said nothing. I was already making plans for the disposal of that obnoxious stuff in the bottle. Several plans were in my mind, but I settled for the most convenient one – that was to tip the medicine down the sink and fill the bottle with cold, black tea. Cold tea was not as bitter as iron, but it was almost as unpleasant to swallow, so when we reached home and Aunt Mary tipped the contents of the bottle down the kitchen sink, I was greatly relieved.

"Debility!" she snorted. "That's what they call everything they can't diagnose!"

So, as one day followed another, I lived in a grey lonely world. Aunt Mary understood so well; she had been there herself. Then one day, when my sorrows seemed to be too much for me, I blurted out, "Why did he have to go so suddenly? Why didn't he tell me he was going? It was all so sudden."

"You must have known he was a visitor," Aunt Mary pointed out, "and I'm sure he gave you a few hints he would not be staying long, but you choose only to hear what you want to hear."

"He kissed me goodbye on the top of my head, and that was all."

"All? Many people go through life without a precious memory like that."

I raised my hand and touched the place on my head where his lips had rested on my hair.

"So that is why you won't have your hair washed!"

I returned her stare without making any reply and she went across to the dresser where a decrepit pair of scissors hung forlornly from a hook. She lifted them down, found a small box, and then came and stood in front of me.

"I'll tell you what," she said, "I'll cut off the hair round that special place and you can keep it as a souvenir, and I can then wash your hair."

Aunt Mary was snipping away when suddenly she saw the scar on my head, and the silence that followed was appalling. Then she began to tremble and the scissors fell from her hand.

"It'll get better," I tried to reassure her, "I only fell."

Buy Aunt Mary could not be convinced and blamed herself in some way or other for negligence. Short of putting an iron ball and chain round my ankle, there was little she could have done. I knew that, and she knew that, but she continued to snip at my hair until she had enough to put into a matchbox. Then I filled the kettle to make the tea (we were not the cocoa type), and Aunt Mary went to the dresser drawer to rout about for something or other. It turned out to be a packet of writing paper, pen and ink, and even an envelope.

When I went to bed that night, I left my aunt writing her letter. She did not look up as I passed her on the way to the door, but I knew well enough that she was weeping.

During the days that followed, Aunt Mary went around with a pale set face and barely said a word. Then came the answer to her letter. It was from my mother to say I was to travel to London by train in care of the guard. Not a long letter, but even if it had been as long as a whole encyclopaedia, it could not possibly have said an appropriate 'thank you' to my Aunt Mary for what were destined to be the happiest years of my life.

That last evening we spent together was far from comfortable; we were not at ease with each other. Her eyes were bright with unshed tears while she did her utmost to be cheerful. I wanted to run to her and hang on to her and implore her not to send me back to my mother and into the unknown. Most of all, I wanted to tell her how much I loved her, for only then did I realise how much. But the words would not come, they stuck in my throat. Maybe it was just as well that I did not tell her; she would have been most affronted.

Oh, all you Aunt Marys of the world, many an unspoken word can be more precious than mere gold!

Late that night, I crept out of the house. The sleeping countryside was dressed in a silver mantle supplied by a large bright moon. It was so beautiful it felt like a slice out of heaven as I made my way towards Harvington. I took in every detail of the surroundings, for instinctively I knew that it would be a long time, if ever, before I would see them again.

Suddenly, standing before me was my beloved house, cradled in the arms of a most magnificent moonlight. Everything was so still; the scars and defacements of time rendered insignificant by the magic of the night. The lovely old house shrouded in ivy, surrounded by ancient trees and encircled within its atmosphere of mystery, ever watching, ever waiting in an unearthly, eerie silence.

So many beautiful and noble houses in the county had disappeared for ever, but Harvington remained, remote, dignified; the very spirit of the place reaching out with a message that no one seemed to understand. Yet in the solitude, there came a feeling of peace, a hint of promise that I did not understand. The blanket of desolation momentarily pushed aside, I walked round the outside of the house, gazing at every detail as though I was committing it to memory.

At last, my steps halted before the fallen tree trunk, my very own tree of knowledge where from the lips of a dear, kind teacher, I had learnt so much. I sat on the ground resting my back against the tree trunk, hands clasped round my knees, chin on chest. For a short time I sat still as a statue, then like a wave, the full realisation of my loss swept over me. Then came the tears, accompanied by sobs that threatened to choke me.

How long I spent in my favourite position by the tree trunk, I never knew, but after a while the tears began to fall more slowly, and the sobs to subside as sleep, that most precious gift from the Almighty, closed my eyes and let me drift away for an hour or two of oblivion.

It was the deepest, most refreshing sleep I could ever remember having and I awoke to a most breathtaking dawn of my life. The sky was ablaze with the most vivid sunrise – all crimson and blue and pink.

Getting to my feet, I walked towards the house to get one last glimpse of it to store in my memory. And there it was before me, never looking more beautiful, more noble, more inspiring with the red sky shining down on its roofs and turning the moat into a sea of fire. The forlorn eerie atmosphere of abandoned places was replaced for one brief moment by one bright gleam of hope. Whatever My Lord had been praying for, I knew that prayer would be answered.

Harvington Hall would rise again.

The Hall from across the moat

Part II

Harvington Regained

The site of the great staircase

Chapter 6

London

M Y SCHOOL was almost opposite the public house called 'The Bricklayer's Arms' in the Old Kent Road. It was called Townsend Street School, and I hated it. My teacher was Miss Olive Sell, and I hated her too. She was very bigoted when she talked to us about religion and history and anybody who did not agree with her views was sneered at. You would have thought that a pretty well educated young lady would be clever enough to see the other person's point of view as well as her own, but Miss Sell did not. She was very plump and well-cared-for-looking, with that aura of peace that can only come from a sense of security and a full belly. When she heard me read, however, she seemed very surprised and signed my form to join the Public Library that stood on the corner of the New Kent Road and Tower Bridge Road.

Among the library assistants there was a lady who was called 'Ivy' by her friends, and she was very kind to me and let me study some of the books that belonged to the adult department of the library, though not to take out, of course. So it chanced that one afternoon in the library, I came upon a precious book, *Forgotten Shrines* by Dom Bede Camm – and to my unutterable joy, there was a whole chapter devoted to Harvington and its glorious martyr, John Wall. There were pictures, too, of the old house just as I knew it, the ivy covering the walls and the various parts of the roof itself. Pictures of the bare brickwork of the walls that had been robbed of their panelling. I sat and gazed until the pages became blurred through the tears that were running down my face. At first, I wanted to rush to Ivy to show her the pictures of my beloved house, but somehow I could not do it. My thoughts and emotions could not be shared with even the kindest of people, so I returned the book to the shelf that it lived on and ran out of the library and did not stop running until I reached home.

My mother had married my first stepfather and I went to live in a fairly big old house in Hilldrop Crescent. My stepfather was quite a nice man. He was an Irishman from Sligo and he worked for the Gainsborough Film Company in Islington as one of the head hair-stylists. He was an ardent Catholic and he always said his prayers. Privately, I thought he was a little soft, but my mother simply adored him, and I can tell you I soon learned that three could be a crowd, but I kept out of the way as much as possible.

My stepfather was devout and my mother had always had a religious kind of veneer, so one day, all three of us went to see one of the priests in our local

Catholic church, and my mother was accepted as a candidate for the Holy See and was to begin her instructions the following week.

One afternoon a year or so later, our 'Miss' (she had a double-barrelled handle actually, Miss Adeline Parker-Prouter, but we all called her 'Miss' till she upset our applecart, then we had a selection of other things to call her) told us to write a composition entitled "My Best Friend". To my great surprise, most of the girls in my class wrote about me being their best friend! They either did not know what a friend really was, or they were trying their hardest to be funny!

That afternoon I really lost myself among my precious memories. Writing my composition about my best friend that afternoon took me back across the miles of telegraph poles, luscious green pastures, cows, streams and beautiful trees, to an old, old house hidden in its covering of green, standing on its island surrounded by its silent moat. Beyond the house to a fallen tree trunk where he was waiting for me – my best friend.

There he sat, every detail of his dear face so clear; his eyes lighting up with welcome when he saw me running across the grass towards him; the smile touching his lips and the sun shining down on his silver hair. Above all things was his voice, carrying in its timbre quietly flowing streamlets, the song of the many birds mingling with the busy sounds of all of earth's most minute and busy insects. Oh, so clearly, I could see him and hear his kind and gentle voice – so much so that I could feel the anguish building up in my head. Thankfully, Miss told us to put down our pens, so I carefully replaced my precious memories in the secret recess of my heart and handed in quite a number of pages about my best friend.

Next morning when I shuffled into the classroom, Miss was already there at her desk and she had our compositions stacked neatly in front of her. As I dragged my feet towards my bench in the back row, Miss halted me with one of her celebrated "Come heres". I took my time in turning round and retracing my reluctant footsteps.

"I have read your essay about your best friend," she told my unfriendly face, "but you have not mentioned the name of your friend. Who was he? What was his name?

For quite a long while I stood and looked at Miss in silence, but it was one of those questions which demands an answer.

"God," I told her briefly but very firmly and, turning my back, I redirected my feet to the back row.

Later on, I joined in the toffee drive organised at the school, with great enthusiasm. For a halfpenny, a penny and (for the rich) tuppence, you could get a bag of glassy-looking toffee of many colours. Red pieces, green lumps, black bits, yellow triangular shapes and many a coloured sliver to tickle the young palate.

It carried me back to the never-to-be-forgotten afternoon among the rafters of Harvington Hall. Once again, I was standing beneath a jagged hole in the roof – one of the sections that was not covered by the ivy that had almost everywhere else in a firm grip. The blue of the heavens above shone in the very same shade of unearthly hue as my piece of toffee. Stranger still, that jagged hole in the roof of Harvington was exactly the same shape as my toffee, only of course many times larger.

The strangest thing of all happened that very same day. Instead of going straight home from school as I normally did, I went to see the priest who almost two years previously had given my mother three months' instruction in the Catholic faith and received her into the Church. At that time he had not appeared very keen to instruct me but I was willing to let bygones be hasbeens if he was. He was. He happened to be having his tea when I rang the bell and disturbed his pleasure. He asked me into the dining room as he returned to a table spread with bread and butter and lashings of delightful strawberry jam. Oh, and plum cake as well, even though the day was not Sunday.

I licked my drooling lips and told him he was having a lovely tea. He rang a small bell and when his 'girl' appeared, he told her to bring some more tea and a plate and cup and saucer, and when she returned with these articles and slapped them down on the table, he asked me what I actually wanted. I told him that I wanted to join the Catholic Church and, naturally enough, he wanted to know why. That was a difficult question to be sure and I needed time to answer. Besides, he was a strict sort of priest who was not given to too much affability, so I resolved to tread warily.

"I have come over all holy, all of a sudden," I told him simply, and strangely enough to my surprise, I found that I was speaking the truth. What was more astonishing still, he believed me.

"What brought it on?"

"This world is a wicked place," I enlightened him.

"So you want to become a Catholic so that you can set the world to rights?" he said very seriously.

"No," I replied, equally as serious as he was. "You see, there is something I have to do."

"Tell me."

Finding the words proved difficult at first, but I soon had the matter in hand. Once I began, the words came tumbling out of my mouth in an avalanche and he let his tea grow cold and his bread and jam he left untouched while he listened in silence.

Across the miles, my heart reached out of my beloved obsession to my dearest Harvington, and I was seeing it once again in my memory as I had seen it so many times. So still, surrounded by green pastures, secluded by many a noble tree, guarded by the dark waters of its moat and all the blemishes inflicted by time hidden beneath its covering of ivy.

The priest sitting opposite me, listening with interest to words gushing from my mouth, the room and its contents, seemed to be suddenly under water as the tears came to my eyes and streamed down my face.

"You see," I wound up very earnestly, "I must learn so many things. I must learn to pray properly, and if I was allowed to go to Holy Communion, I would be so close to Our Lord – I would know what to say to Him …"

"Child," said the priest seriously, "it is no easy decision for anyone to make. Our Lord promised nobody happiness in this world, especially not to His friends and followers. The blind and the deaf, the lame and the sick who sought Him were sent on their way after He had cured them."

I bowed my head and let my chin press against my chest as I thought over his words.

He went on in a very kind sort of voice, "The best way to pray is first close your eyes tightly so that you are in complete darkness. Then stretch out your arms across that darkness and Almighty God will take your hands in His and He will know what is in your heart and send you consolation."

After a short while, I managed a watery smile and a bite of bread and jam.

"That is better," said the priest, who also began on his interrupted meal.

"I will come to your house to have a talk with your people," he promised when he had shown me to the door. "Meanwhile, I shall give the matter a great deal of thought."

He kept his promise, and, three evenings later, he was the guest of honour at our house. I was not permitted to stay and listen to the debate or whatever it was, but when at last it was over, I was sent for and told that I was to begin taking my instructions the following week. I was to go to the presbytery two afternoons after school every week to learn about the Faith I was so anxious to join.

My stepfather was elated. When the priest, whose name turned out to be the Reverend Thomas FitzGerald, had departed from our midst, my stepfather took me out to the back garden and cut off my rat's tail hair and gave me what was known as an 'Eton crop'.

Father FitzGerald was a very strict taskmaster. He made me learn the penny catechism from cover to cover by heart. I had to learn a certain number of the questions and answers of that catechism ready for our next session at the presbytery. And you had to know those answers thoroughly, for he had a very short way with those who did not chirp up readily and brightly with what he was waiting to hear. You had better not let your attention wander either, because he thought nothing of giving you a sharp smart slap on the back of your hand to bring you back to the matter of the moment. The day I told him that Our Lord died on Mount Blanc, he almost hit the roof, but he sent me home in disgrace instead.

Six months it took that priest to convert me. He worked with patience through my amazing number of 'whys' and always seemed able to satisfy my curiosity in his replies – well, most of them anyway.

At the end of my instruction, Father FitzGerald received me into the Church. As I was a child, I did not have to say the long act of Faith at the altar rails; I said the short one and afterwards I was given conditional Baptism with my head under the tap of the sacristy sink. As the priest dried his hands on the towel that was hanging near the sink, he told my mother and stepfather that I was his first child convert and I couldn't help noticing that the tone of his voice suggested that he hoped I would be the last.

When I went up at last to receive Our Lord, I shut my eyes so that I could be in that darkness. I reached out my hands – and there he stood on the bridge that spanned the moat, the sun lighting up his silvery hair. His steady blue eyes twinkling and the beautiful crucifix on his breast dazzling in the glow of the morning.

Father FitzGerald was right. I had closed my eyes, reached out with my hands and touched God.

Of course he was God.

The South garden, with the Malt-House and Georgian Chapel

Chapter 7

Liverpool

"PROMISE ME," said my mother, as we turned in at the convent gate, "that you will not use any bad language." I promised. As a matter of fact, I had never used bad words since the day at Harvington when My Lord had pointed out the ugliness of expletives in general.

"And you will try not to be rough or rude," went on my mother, as we made our way up the drive.

I promised.

They were happy days as I finished my schooling in the Convent overlooking Hampstead Heath, but they could not blot out the longing for Aunt Mary, Oo-la-la and Ichee-Koo and my enchanting house nestling in its mantle of ivy. I could never stifle the longing for them when I came across a house or building of mellow red brick and doors of ancient oak shining through gaps of clinging vines.

One particular Sunday was the most wonderful, the most heavenly of my Sundays. Through the haze of incense, I saw, not the hands of our kindly chaplain, but the long slender hands of My Lord that last day when we knelt on the stairs that concealed the small hidden room where Father Wall had so often taken refuge.

He had covered his face when he prayed that day, and this day I covered my face with happiness for our prayers had been answered. Harvington Hall was to be saved from the dust, from oblivion that had befallen so many of the famous, splendid ancient houses.

Among my letters that afternoon, there was one from my Aunt Mary to tell me that my lovely house, my Harvington Hall, had been bought from the Throckmortons by a lady who gave it to the diocese of Birmingham to be restored and used as a shrine.

Most of the girls in my year passed their Matriculation examination. Indeed, quite a number of them passed with honours, but I passed with a headache. Nevertheless, I passed. My stepfather was delighted; my mother was very surprised, but I think she was glad that my stepfather had not wasted his money on me.

The person who was happiest of all at that time was me, because I was asked what I would like for a present for passing my exam. My reply had been prompt and most decisive. I wanted to go to Worcestershire to see my Aunt Mary, Oo-la-la and Ichee-Koo. My mother was still more surprised; knowing me, she thought I would at least ask for five thousand a year and a motor car!

68

So it was arranged for me to spend the remainder of the long summer holiday in Kidderminster with my "family", but, most of all, most truly above all, I would see the house so dear to my heart.

At last, arrived at the station, there was my Aunt Mary and Ichee-Koo standing at her side. We looked at each other without saying a word for quite a while, and she was the first to speak at last. "So here you are, then," she said.

"Yes, Aunt Mary, here I am." Then I bent down and made a huge fuss of Ichee-Koo. More than half of the kissing and hugging was meant for my aunt, of course, but she would have been very offended at any kind of demonstration, so that is why I poured it all out on the little dog. Nevertheless, we were both most happy to see each other. I handed her the bag of things my mother had sent her and an envelope my stepdad had told me to give her, and the three of us turned towards our village and Aunt Mary's cottage. Nothing was changed in the years I had been away. Oo-la-la, though, had grown very thin and frail, but she still ruled the little household from her throne on the velvet cushion. Aunt Mary still spread a couple of sheets of newspaper on the table for a cloth, and we used the same old enamel mugs to drink our tea from. I had not tasted such delicious tea for five long years. And we had kippers cooked as only my aunt knew how.

After the meal, when we had all taken our places by the fire, she began to talk about Harvington Hall. "There is not much to tell," she began reflectively, "for it was not touched for a long time. After vandals had broken in and done a great deal of damage, the gaps in walls were repaired and doors and windows made more secure from intruders." When she said 'intruders', she gave me a most meaning look from the corners of her eyes.

"What is happening now?"

"They are stripping the ivy from the chimneys and roof – I suppose they will have to repair the roof soon, before it caves in."

The roof. Stealing out of my mind came pictures of My Lord with their precious memories, the lonely garrets with the wind crying eerily through the rafters; the walkway right up in the apex of the roof where fugitives of past days could crawl along the length and breadth of the old mansion without touching a passage or floor of the house.

So Harvington Hall was being shorn of its mantle of green. I wondered what she looked like – probably she would put the observers in mind of an old, old lady at the public baths and wash-house, waiting for a clean-up.

Aunt Mary must have read my thoughts.

"Very little of the ivy has been removed so far – it must be costing a great deal of money, and they say the stems of the ivy are as thick as tree trunks."

"I shall go to see it myself, very early in the morning," I told her.

"I know you will," replied my Aunt Mary, "but it will be better if you go by way of the home farm this time – some of your neat little short cuts have been built on. You can't put your big foot in somebody's breakfast egg."

And there it was, shrouded in the mist of early morning. The old familiar lump came into my throat as it always did when I stood and beheld it. Some of the growth on the roof and round the chimneys had been removed, probably at the request of a surveyor, but the abandoned look seemed to have vanished with the air of hopelessness. I could tell that My Lord's prayers were being answered. A feeling of great joy swept over me, but at the same time, that old urge I felt in the Great Chamber and the compelling desire to take up a pen and write and write seeped into my spirit again as it did when, five years before, I had stood in Doctor Dodd's Library. And me, a very ignorant fifteen-year-old. Certainly I had love enough, but I was lacking in years. Surely it would take a lifetime of experience and emotion before I could attempt to put my pen to paper.

The red brickwork and bared patches on the roof and chimneys seemed to glow as the sun got well under way in the heavens and the sweet sedge began to send out its own particular fragrance, whilst on the tiles of the low roofs on the oldest part of the house, great clusters of polypody fern harmonised beautifully with the ancient bricks. A perfect morning it was, and I made my way to my fallen tree trunk where I had learned so much of wisdom, of loyalty, suffering and devotion. Momentarily, the desolation of my loss enveloped me, but when it passed and I was sitting in my accustomed place on the ground, leaning my back against the trunk, hands clasped about knees, chin on chest and eyes firmly closed, the whole procession of them – Father John Wall, at the head of the band, followed by Fathers Garnet, Oldcorne, Southwell, Postgate, Barlow, Gerard, Campion, and many another; but my heroes brought up the rear, Nicholas Owen carrying his lantern and bag of tools, his expression taciturn as he could make it, and at his side, the other lay brother, Ralph Ashley.

Perhaps the Reformation was necessary, who was I to say? The Church and the religious establishments were growing too slack and too wealthy, but the Faith itself was in no need of a reform. To my fifteen-year-old mind, it seemed that the monasteries were dissolved and their treasures shared by the king and his friends, and all the nice comfortable bits of the old Faith kept and adhered to, while all the disagreeable practices were thrown out. The king became the Head of the new Church, with his cosy outlook of "Don't do as I do – do as I tell you".

Father FitzGerald, when he was instructing me in the Catholic doctrine, told me that the difference between the old church and the reformed one was in a word – transubstantiation in the holy Eucharist of the ancient faith, and consubstantiation in the new. Any decent dictionary will explain those words: as I said in the beginning, this is not a religious book.

Time passed, but I sat there wallowing in memories and dreams and longings of five years of exile. The quest that began on my first visit when I had stood in the Great Chamber, cheek pressed against the wall, seemed to be tugging at my heart and mind trying to impart a message that I was too young to understand. Of one thing I was sure. Never in my life would I ever forget my beautiful Harvington Hall.

* * * *

In the autumn of that year when I visited my Aunt Mary and Harvington, I was sent as a boarder to St. Vincent's Convent, Carlisle Place, Westminster. My days there seemed to speed by, and I passed, first, my Junior Oxford, and then my Senior Oxford, and so became eligible to apply for a place in a teachers' training college. The one I selected was in the north-west of England, not too far from my Aunt Mary, and, to my great joy, I was accepted.

Those three years of training in the dockland of Liverpool I found strenuous and often exhausting; times there were when I would have cheerfully given up and gone back home, but there was this magnetic force within me that spurred me on, this quest born on that first day I had stepped into Harvington Hall. All I knew for certain was that Harvington had some kind of task waiting for me to do, but I would often ask myself what an ancient house of secrets and a past shrouded in mysterious silence, with much of its history lost in the mist of time, wanted of a young and ignorant person as I was. It was one of my everlasting 'why's?' I could not find an answer to, so I put my heart and back into my studies with the knowledge that I was preparing myself with experience to begin my enduring quest – to seek some means of telling the world of a gem that had not ceased its shining throughout the years.

Often, I snatched an hour or two at Harvington, and sat in my accustomed attitude close to my old and decaying tree trunk and meditated in solitude, for very little so far had been done towards restoring the house. The ivy, of which little had been removed, still clung tenaciously to the windows and warm red walls, reminding me of many a ghost and a myriad of echoes.

Lady Mary Yate often occupied my thoughts. There, in Chaddesley Corbett church, stands her tomb in the North Chapel dedicated to St. Nicholas where her earthly remains lie surrounded by those of her family. Her epitaph was a beautiful one, written by her devoted daughter, Apollonia Yate. The outstanding words "Her fortitude was built upon her faith, a rock which no storm could move." So apt a tribute to the hostess of Harvington's own saint. Thinking of the hiding-places in the old mansion, those known, many never discovered, the hole in the woodwork where a pursuivant had fired at her, yes, those outstanding words were very apt indeed.

So my three years of training passed. I was home with my mother and my stepdad when I received the news that I had passed my final tests with credits.

The Malt House

My satisfaction, I knew, would be but moonlight as to sunlight compared to the happiness that would be felt by my stepfather, who had always shown confidence in my ability. So he was going to be the first to know of my success. It was a day when he was home on leave from the studios and he was tending his beloved roses in the garden.

Dashing out to him, I suddenly halted. There was a deathly premonition taking a grip on me. He was lying face downwards, so very still. So unearthly still.

When, at length, I moved towards him, I gently turned him over, and reverently closed his eyes. The lamp was still there, but the light had burnt out.

Chapter 8

Midsomer St. Mary

AFTER I had finished my training in the north-west of the country, I stayed up there and taught in the schools in the dockland area of Liverpool, staying with Aunt Mary at the weekends and for holidays until she died. Oo-la-la went first, to be followed shortly after by Ichee-Koo. When my aunt joined them, I returned to London and took to the enlightening of the little minds of Lambeth. I loved the Liverpool children, but I am sure the Lambeth scholars taught me far more than I ever taught them.

During this period, the ivy had been stripped from windows, roofs and walls of Harvington Hall, giving it an unfamiliar, undressed kind of look, and the urgent repairs to the roof and structure of the building were still being taken care of, but so far, the actual work of restoration did not seem to have begun. What the owners intended to do with the house, I was told, was to turn it into a shrine to the memory of the many martyrs who died for their beliefs, and to enkindle the flame that seemed to have died for a short spell in England.

Christ promised that the gates of Hell should never prevail against His Church; He said that He would remain with her till the end of the world, and He surely must have been with her or those courageous souls who walked hand in hand with imprisonment and torture every hour of the day, or they could never have survived the test. So much love and devotion and bloodshed mingled with anguish and suffering. Indeed, there should be a shrine to their memory. It should be Harvington Hall.

So many of the stately mansions that gave sanctuary to the hunted priests and recusants have disappeared beneath the dust. Hindlip House, the most stately, most beautiful of structures, was the home of John Habington, who was Queen Elizabeth's treasurer of the household. Soon after he bought Hindlip, one of his sons was hanged for his complicity in the Babington Plot to set Mary, Queen of Scots, on the throne of England. Then another son, Thomas, was pardoned. No less than eleven hiding-holes were fitted at Hindlip by Nicholas Owen, but it was at this house that Nicholas Owen was starved out of one of his own hiding places, together with Fathers Oldcorne and Garnet, and lay brother Ralph Ashley. They were betrayed by Humphrey Littleton.

Only a small part of Huddington Court is left now, but it was a remarkably beautiful mansion belonging to the Wyntour family until it passed from their possession at the end of the seventeenth century. The Wyntours – their Welsh name meant 'White Tower' – were noted recusants and connected with all the leading Catholic families. Two members of the family died because of their part in the Gunpowder Plot, and also the schoolboy son of the house who had nothing to do with the Plot was killed. The old Huddington Court was reputed to be haunted by Robert Wyntour's ghost carrying its head along the corridors, whilst that of his wife had often been seen pacing the passage to the door awaiting the return of her husband.

To the north of Huddington Court, in Staffordshire, was the lovely mansion of tragic memory where the Gunpowder Plotters made their last stand. Their powder being damp, they took it into Holbeach House to dry it near the fire. There was a terrific explosion and the house was in flames. The Wyntours and their fellow conspirators were captured here and paid with their lives.

In the south-west of Worcestershire stands Pickersleigh Court; that house has a second name, still remembered by many local people, 'Seven Sheets'. It is a name handed down from penal days when the faithful were informed by signs and secret signals when a service was to be held. Many a recusant house used this method to convey the day and time of the celebration of Mass by hanging linen over hedges. If it was to be the third day of the week, they would put out three sheets and arrange smaller articles in patterns to denote the time.

It was in the spring of 1939 when that flibberty-jibberty thing we often allude to as 'chance' steered my steps towards another old and mouldering house, standing on the outskirts of a village that was cosily tucked into a luscious pocket of green countryside. A quiet, unworldly-seeming little spot, yet within easy access to the station and London.

The original colour of the walls was grey, and of the window-frames white, like the balustrades surrounding the roof and terraces. There was a beautiful octagonal tower on each of the four corners of the roof. Right in the middle of the roof was a large glass dome, and as I stood there gazing at the time-worn façade of the house, I knew I had to find a way in and explore what must once have been a very gem of a house set in the style of Inigo Jones.

Time and weather had almost obliterated the name of the house from the dilapidated gateposts, so it took me quite some time before I was able to decipher the words, but eventually I was able to make out the word 'Midsomer' on one pillar and 'St. Mary's' on the other. Midsomer St. Mary. I kept on repeating the lovely name as I walked up the long drive and was still rolling it round my tongue when I came to a halt before the main door of the house.

But this truly lovely jewel of architecture was not in any way to be compared with Harvington Hall. In spite of its abandonment, its neglect and decay, Harvington was a living house – call them what you like, ghosts, spirits, memories – they kept the house of this world as well in it. Midsomer St. Mary, however, seemed quite dead as far as atmosphere was concerned: the only sounds of life came from tiny throats behind the wainscot.

Following discussions with my friend Bishop Brown, it was agreed that I could open Midsomer St. Mary as a small private school to take my catechism class in as evacuees, which I did in May 1939. The authorities had inspected the premises thoroughly and granted me a permit to take twelve little pupils, and they warned me not to exceed that number, threatening to revoke my licence if I disregarded the stipulation.

Happy days – especially when I stole the odd moments to hide in my turret and dream a brief dream or two. It really was a secret place; the way in was through a door in the wainscot on the top corridor and up a flight of curly stairs. In some mysterious way, it seemed to bring Harvington Hall closer. When I gazed out of any of the eight long narrow windows, I had a magnificent view over the sadly neglected grounds. I could have been surveying the grounds of Harvington, but my tree trunk of knowledge was not there.

So many years had gone by, so much light and shade had crept in and mingled with my memories, but nothing had dimmed my recollection of my wonderful teacher. I had only to close my eyes and there he was, the sun making his hair shine; I had but to listen and I heard his voice. Yes, he must have been God.

Some days at Midsomer St. Mary were happy enough, when everything seemed to run smoothly, but sometimes life could be sheer hell. These latter times used to mostly occur on Mondays when a gang of women from the village came to do the washing. Mind you, nursery towels were child's play to wash compared with the garments that had been worn by the Toffs for a day or two. These ladies of the wash tubs had plenty to complain about and they by no means suffered in silence. The house was filled with a kind of noise that sounded like a continuous humming of the seven penitential psalms.

On these occasions, when the opportunity presented itself, I would sneak up to my little turret room, away from all the turmoil, and would travel back over the years to Harvington.

I knew that the old house had undergone change. The ivy had been stripped from walls and windows, and new roofs replaced the old ones. Unsafe floors were gradually attended to and the long process of restoration and repair was in hand. The charm of ruin had, I supposed, to be sacrificed in the name of preservation. An undressed, cleaned up façade of Harvington was more comfortable to the beholder than a pile of rubble. The moat had been cleaned up and uncluttered since the last time my eyes had beheld it, and two beautiful swans had made their home on its shining waters. Yet in spite of its new lease of life, the deep sense of sadness remained; unseen eyes peered from the large windows, and many a sigh echoed from the house to the encircling trees.

I did not go into the house itself, there was no point in making myself ache any more than I was aching then.

In the long intervals between my visits, memories of Harvington stayed fresh in my memory, even through the darkest days of war. Yes, I loved my little bolt-hole high up in the turret.

How well I remember that day which I thought was to be my last. It began on a cool blue morning with the sun taking over from a waning moon, when there was a hush all over the countryside, shattered only by the call of cockerels and stirring birds. How many mornings like it had I awakened to, letting it pass with indifference, taking for granted that it was the beginning of another day?

That night, when the chores of my day at Midsomer St. Mary were finished, I travelled up to London to be with my mother as was my usual custom. I expected to find her alone in the house with her wireless set and her crochet work, so I was very surprised when I found my stepfather (my mother had married again within a year of my first stepfather's death) was still in the house.

After the customary glare had passed between us, he explained that the cold my mother had developed a day or so earlier had turned into pneumonia, and that in no circumstances was she to leave her bed. He picked up his hat, and I ran up the stairs to the bedroom on the third floor, trying in vain to still my heart that seemed to have turned into a yo-yo between my ribs.

It was an ugly old house on the corner of Riverhall Street and Hartington Road. A flimsy old building and no mistake, with creaking doors and noisy floorboards, to say nothing of the rattling windows and shaking walls. It was obvious to the meanest intellect that a gust of strong wind could cause it to disintegrate, unless a bomb got in first and tore it apart.

Taking up his walking stick, he was out of the place before I reached the top landing. How I hated that old man! I felt that I did not hate him enough for the years of misery my mother had lived with him and the way she had worked and slaved to keep him after the brewers had had his licence taken from him after dragging him through the bankruptcy court. He had taken what little jewellery she had possessed and sold it to pay for his double whiskies, and he had given his family all her cherished possessions from the past. But she only mildly protested, because she thought nobody was perfect.

Just for a moment, a wave of pity seemed to be engulfing me as I stood in that doorway looking towards the small pathetic bundle on the bed. I stood there and prayed from the depths of my heart that there would not be an air raid that night, but hardly had I begun before the siren began to wail. I felt sick with terror. Nobody knew how frightened I was in the raids on London. I was an abject coward, my faith in God was at its lowest ebb, but on this night of nights, my fear was at its height. Accompanied by an awful premonition of danger, was the overwhelming desire to run screaming down those mean little stairs and out to the brick shelter in Riverhall Street.

One look at my mother, who was so desperately ill, made me to to the bedside and sit as close to her as I could, taking her hand into mine, hoping the warmth would still the trembling of my hand and not let my fear communicate itself to her. But she was not unconscious. She croaked out the word "Go," and in a voice that I did not recognise as my own, I said, "Not likely," and I was glad to know that I meant it.

It turned out to be a filthy night, with the enemy planes coming over in fast relays, spilling anguish, heartbreak, devastation and agony from the skies, just as the life blood was being shed in Germany by innocent women and their children.

The house shuddered every time a bomb landed, adding to the number of big craters already decorating the district. People said you never heard the whine of a bomb if it had your name written on it, but take it from me, I heard the thing coming down whining all right. My name was not on it, but the names of many of the neighbours I knew were inscribed on the thing leaving no room for my mother's name or mine, but we came very close to being included. I clasped my mother's hand more tightly as the thing touched the ground and the sickening roar of the explosion almost shattering the eardrums and the blast that demolished the house would have put a hundred and ninety miles per hour hurricane to shame.

The terrific impact, together with the sensation of turning cartwheels on a wheelbarrow (my dear stepdad always told me that I could charm the heart of a wheelbarrow in order to get my own way) caused me to close my eyes and drift off to blessed oblivion. How long I was unconscious, I could not tell, for a thick blanket of darkness seemed to be smothering me and the silence was unbearable. I wanted to call out for my mother, but some instinct seemed to warn me not to do so, because I was pinned down by a heavy weight lying across my arms and chest near enough to my windpipe to impede my breathing, and another obstacle was spread across my legs so that I could not move. If any more rubble came down on top of me, I think it would have put me out of my misery, for by this time the cramp was beginning to torture me and I wanted to change my position, but I could not move and my muscles had reached a pitch past screaming and the pain, pure agony.

From my heart I prayed to God. Broken fragments from prayers I had learned over the years, the parts of the psalms I had learned to love dearly, though not as much as I loved them on that never to be forgotten night. Words of my own mingled with them " 'For if Thou, O Lord, shalt observe iniquities, who shall endure it.' Dear God, I don't want to die. 'For with Thee there is merciful forgiveness.' Please God, let me know what I am to do if you really did put us in the world to serve you. 'From the morning watch, even until night, let Israel hope in the Lord.' Dear God, I hope in you. Don't forsake me now. I do not want to die."

The terrible thirst and the thick smell of broken plaster was overwhelming, but it reminded me of Harvington Hall, and the same sensation that assailed me all those years before when I had so nearly met my end on the courtyard via a broken door was with me now, but this time I understood in a small way something of the suffering and endurance of our brave recusant priests who took refuge in hiding-places, some of which were too small to allow a person to stand upright or to sit down to stretch his legs. And this for days that could, on occasion, last into weeks, as well the hunger and thirst and the bitter cold, followed by capture in many cases, and a brutal, most hideous death on the scaffold at the end of their endeavour.

So much has been said about the cruelty and barbarity of Queen Mary and her fanatic devotion to the Faith, but little enough has been mentioned about the recusants and the blood they shed for their cause, and Topcliffe and company motivated by greed and a great love of money. Bigotry, I saw in my own most tormented mind that night, was one of the main causes of misery in this world, causing a dirty blemish to form on the face of civilisation. To my mind, it seemed that most bigotry began in high places. In the top places they found it easy enough to coerce the low and the ignorant and dependents, to say nothing of the 'what's in it for me' contingent, into following their line of thought. One should not pry into the private thoughts of an individual, but I often wonder why James I hated the recusants so much (apart from the Gunpowder Plot, which understandably rattled him), when, after all, his own mother, the tragic Mary, Queen of Scots, was such a devoted adherent to the old religion.

The last vivid picture in my aching head before I went drifting off to oblivion again was of Harvington Hall, its Elizabethan façade reflected in the waters of the moat. I dreamed I was lying in a small rowing boat drifting on the moat, pressed by the great weight that would not let me move, hardly letting me breathe. We moved slowly across the moat and entered a wider expanse of water shrouded by many tall dark trees standing like sentinels along the margin of the bank. When my tiny craft came to a halt beneath the shadow of the tree, I became free of the load that had been pinning me down and I was able to move once again. Before I disembarked, I looked carefully up at that tree, whose splendid branches overhung my landing place; there seemed to be something so familiar about its trunk. The ground I found myself standing on was not flat, as it should have been, but inclined gradually upwards, and the grass beneath my feet was of the softest, most heavenly shade of green.

Then I saw the figure silhouetted against the sky.

A deep sense of peace came over me. It was an unearthly, ethereal feeling that was sweeping over me as I slowly moved towards the figure's outstretched hand. His face was hidden in gossamer mists, white and silky and like the shining hair I remembered and loved so dearly. Of course he was God – I always said he was.

In that merest fraction of time, I saw a glimpse of Heaven, and when he took my hand into his, I knew what the quest was that I was groping for. I knew, too, that the day would dawn when I would be worthy to attempt it.

When consciousness returned, I was in hospital, and my mother was holding my hand. She explained that we had been rescued from the ruins of the house after two days. We were taken to St. Thomas's Hospital where my mother made a good recovery. My own recovery was a little more protracted as I had developed a tumour on the back of my right eye which needed surgery. It was some little time before I was pronounced fit.

Chapter 9

Fountains

M Y MOTHER had been granted a requisitioned little shop on a street corner at the end of the street we had been bombed out of, and as it was not too far from his beloved pub, my stepfather thoroughly approved of it.

In the months that followed, when Europe was overrun by the allies, it was quite obvious that the war was drawing to an end. One afternoon, all being quiet with an atmosphere of peace pervading the whole place, I crept up to my turret and stood by the window, gazing down at the grounds yet not seeing them. Soon life at St. Mary's would be coming to a close. Soon, Midsomer St. Mary would become a casualty of the peace. I placed a hand on the window ledge and the other hand on top of it, a habit of mine when I wanted to pray.

Closing my eyes, I began to take stock of myself. I was now thirty-five years old, and I had not begun my quest. I had not fulfilled that overpowering desire to make that ancient house, my beloved Harvington Hall, better known to the world of prejudice. Its full history perhaps may never come to light, but its fascinating air of mystery is doubtless its greatest charm.

I had never gone back to Harvington since the restoration had begun because it was not the same. The beauty of ruin would have gone for ever with the masses of ivy that had clung to the house's roofs and windows. The sighing wind through ancient rafters would by now have been silenced. Yet it could not destroy the spirit of the house, nor could it blot out the quiet ghosts of a long-gone past.

Above all else, it could not still the urge in my heart and mind to show Harvington Hall as it was, as seen through the eyes of a ten-year-old child, when the hand of neglect lay over it and deep shadows lingered in its forsaken rooms and forgotten passages. The bewitching atmosphere of mystery that pervaded the entire house, conveying some urgent request, some overwhelming feeling of voices in the dark corners, desperately seeking to pass on a message.

The early dusk was settling over everything, but I still stood at the turret window, seeing only a vision of the old house shrouded in its cloak of ivy. Then it came to me, what I should do for Harvington, to share with others who cared for the history of ancient houses, who had a special kind of interest in oak beams and old stonework, but, above all, for the memory of those who died rekindling the flame of Faith in a land that was deep in darkness.

St. Paul's Churchyard is the spot where Father Henry Garnet died. A public garden, surrounded by iron railings, affords an oasis of peace and seclusion away from the bustle of Ludgate Hill. It takes up a sizeable slice of the churchyard, but it contains the ruins of the old cloisters and the remains of the chapter house of the old St. Paul's destroyed in the Great Fire in 1666. Small, but significant, reminders that a wall had enclosed the churchyard, erected by order of Edward I to keep the bad people out, are alleys representing the positions of the posterns: St. Paul's Alley, Canon Alley with a pump in the roadway, and, going a little way down Ludgate Hill, I saw Creed Lane on my left and Ave Maria Lane on my right. Ava Maria Lane leads to Paternoster Row, where, turning left and passing through a wooden gateway, I found myself in Amen Court.

That was truly a wonderful spot to end up in. With link extinguishers outside its eighteenth-century houses, it is mostly occupied by minor canons of the cathedral.

The afternoon was fading into evening, the hurrying footsteps of typists and clerks, the high-ups and the humble were making for the overcrowded transport that would carry them home. But I lingered in that hallowed spot until a pleasant hush descended over the churchyard, when the last of the starlings had located its territory and the indignant squawking had subsided. Then I had a little word with him whose blood had sanctified the place where I was resting.

"Father Garnet," I prayed, "intercede for me before God's throne and ask of Him a blessing on my undertaking of a task I am not worthy to perform."

Then my holy solo broke down, so I continued my one-sided conversation as dictated from my heart. "You see, Father Garnet, it's like this," I told him, "I am not a saintly person. When I go to confession, the penance the priest gives me to say is a long one, which shows that I am not worthy to write a book about saints. Although you martyrs do have the title of 'Blessed', it is not enough; you should be canonised, each one of you who died for the Cause. Yet how can I begin on such a project? I am so ordinary and very ignorant.'

The sky had deepened to dark blue, and a myriad of stars shone down, but I did not see the walls of weathered Portland stone. They seemed to have been replaced by rich, red brickwork reflected in the waters of the moat before them – Harvington Hall. An overwhelming wave of love mingled with almost unbearable anguish engulfed my entire senses as I saw the white-haired figure standing there at the entrance of the Hall, the shining crucifix on his breast. His visit to the old house, brief though it was, must have had a purpose.

September 1945 came, bringing with it the cool touch of autumn, with the green of summer turning to red and gold, and I stood outside the gates of Midsomer St. Mary, keys in hand, watching a white mist rising from the ground. The last of the evacuees had gone. I stood alone taking leave of the beautiful old house. After that, I worked as a supply teacher for three years under the London County Council. Not a bad life if you liked variety, and I have always got on well with children, provided I kept one step ahead of them. Some teachers prayed for an abundance of grace from Above, but personally, I would have settled for a pop gun and adequate ammunition to be used on some of the head teachers.

All of them excepting a head from Yorkshire, name of Greenwood, based in a school near the Walworth Road, put me in mind of a bag of nails, all shapes and sizes and mostly pretty sharp on the uptake and in the tongue. But Mr. Greenwood was out of a different stable altogether. I only worked for him for three weeks and on the last day I went to his office-cum-storeroom to bid him goodbye. He gave me a handsome smile that would have outshone an autumn sunset, and, breaking into broad Yorkshire, he told me that I was a 'gradely' teacher, and if I wanted a permanent place in his school, "Tha can coom 'ere." I did not repeat the famous words of G. B. Shaw's Eliza Doolittle, but my pump-handle shake of the hand must have conveyed the warmth of a downtrodden under-privileged supply, who was feeling like Lazarus picking up a crumb or two from the rich man's table.

The flat I had was most conveniently placed. There was a bus stop outside our entrance, a market just beyond the backyards, and, finest asset of all, three blocks of flats away there was a handsome library, as I think I have already mentioned, which became almost my second home. The flat was on the top floor at the end of all four blocks, and narrowing to a round shaped end, there were four rooms facing the front, and the bathroom, kitchen, larder and coal hole were situated at the back, the windows commanded a magnificent view of the Battersea gasworks. The corridor of the flat was exactly thirty-three feet in length; the kitchen was at the street door end and the large living room-cum-lounge was situated at the other. This living room had two ordinary sash windows, one on the front wall from whence could be obtained an interesting picture of a wood-yard and an old mansion with a clock-tower beyond it. It was the registered offices of a well known vinegar brewery. I had a queer sort of affinity with that old house, expecially on days when, like Job, my sorrows were too much for me and I felt sure I must have been weaned on vinegar myself. But dearest window of all was in the end wall, where a kind of intimate glimpse could be had of the south-facing dial of Big Ben and the sound of him when the wind was in the right direction.

The floors of my funny old flat were sloping at rather an alarming degree, thanks to a high explosive bomb that had settled in the vicinity, so it gave one the impression of living at sea. Even so, what could you expect for a weekly rent of fifteen shillings and three halfpence? And that was not all. Added to all this bliss, I shared a triangular-shaped bit of flat roof railed on two sides by very rusty railings, and by staring between them you got an interesting vista of pickle factory, pocket-handkerchief park and a double row of little backyards and bungalow zinc baths hanging on the outside toilet walls. Many a dad or grandad I spied on Sunday mornings slinking into these toilets with a newspaper tucked underneath an arm to seek a spot that offered peace from the Sunday turmoil of their happy homes.

The tenants of these flats were mostly friendly, but wherever you moor your bones, you will get people who cannot possibly be happy unless they are miserable. There was one man who had a flat three flights down in the same block I lived in. He was an actor on the music hall stages. A well known character he was, but I, privately, called him 'Gladys' since the first time I met him on the stairs outside his flat. He was wearing a pink frilly pinny, a scarf over his head, and he paused in his tickling of his front door with a feather duster to bid me "Good morning, dearie," in a high-pitched girlie sort of tone. Returning the greeting, I was about to depart, when he said, "When I have finished my dusting, I must wash my smalls." Yes, well it takes all kinds to make a world. Gladys and I became firm friends.

Outside the buildings in the fresh air, I would point my nose in the direction of Vauxhall en route for St. Anne's Church where my dear Bishop Brown lay at rest beneath the floor of the Mortuary Chapel, where he had slept every night through the bombing of London. Had I been asked to write an epitaph to him, I should have simply had inscribed, "His bark was worse than his bite". The church was very quiet, but perhaps the peace I always felt in my heart and soul blotted out the noise of traffic and the business of living belonged to the world beyond the stout doors. Then there was the smell that pervaded the atmosphere of the church, a blend of Marmite and incense. The Marmite factory was near to the church. Of all the churches I have visited, never have I ever encountered such an extraordinary odour: it was not one of sanctity, but after a deep gulp or two, I found it to be the closest thing to it.

Strangely enough, after a one-sided chat with the bishop, I left St. Anne's with the same satisfied feeling that I always had after sharing his pot of tea with him.

* * * *

The year was 1970, and on the twenty-fifth day of October that year, Blessed John Wall, beloved martyr of Harvington, together with thirty-nine other martyrs of England and Wales, was canonised. That night I was standing on my small triangle of roof trying to sort the ragbag of my mind. Reflecting somewhat sombrely that I was going to be sixty years old at Christmas time, and that this solitary sorting out in my rooftop eyrie was to be my last, for within a few hours, a removal van was going to park outside while a couple of stalwarts threw in the bits and pieces that had made up my home for the past years, preparatory to removing all traces of the tenant who was departing for a semi-detached in Finchley. My thoughts were indeed rather solemn.

The canonisation of the martyrs of England and Wales had caused much rejoicing and celebration during the day, but it all left me still wondering why it had taken the Holy Apostolic See so long to have them raised to the Altar of God. Why?

And another 'why' came into my head; I asked myself why I was taking so long to set down on paper the story of an ancient house so dear to the heart of a misfit. Big Ben, the lights of St. Thomas's Hospital and the bits and bobs of the intervening buildings faded into insignificance as memory conjured up a picture of 'My Harvington Hall'. The picture was so vivid that I grasped the rusty railings in such a tight grip as if I was clutching at the proverbial straw in the hands of a drowning man. It was the Harvington of my childhood with its masses of ivy clinging to the walls and windows where, on windy days, a lament could be heard sighing through the garrets. As the years came and went, I had travelled to as many shrines hallowed by sufferings of the English and Welsh martyrs as I could, and to holy places of retreat and prayer to savour the deep joy and peace so far removed from the bustling, busy world of up and coming motor cars and television sets. Yet not once had I returned to Harvington.

One day, late in the afternoon, whilst in Yorkshire, I came upon the seclud-ed manor of Markenfield Hall. The exteriors of these ancient stately homes seemed to me to be more attractive than the rooms behind their splendid facades, so I did not see the interior. The sight of the beautiful, gracious building, in its setting of magnificent trees, was sufficient for me. Besides, it was getting on for twilight, and I had another little pilgrimage to make while I was in the district.

So I turned my steps towards the north-west where a two mile walk through lovely parkland and secluded tracks led me to the ruins of Fountains Abbey. It has been said by many that the ruins of Fountains are the most beautiful and best preserved in the kingdom, but I think they are the most wonderful in the world. To see them at their best is when the sky is growing dark and deep violet shadows steal out from remaining cloisters and a brilliant moon sailing in the sky turns the broken arches into aesthetic silver. If animals and the little creatures of the night are your friends, and you stand alone and lis-ten to the assortment of sounds issuing from them, your ears become attuned and your senses enthrall to a nocturnal litany chanted by human throats of centuries past.

Since I was a youngish woman recovering from the operation on my eyes, I had never been able to kneel down without a nauseating attack of giddiness when the floor changed places with the ceiling. I was told this misery occurred because a duct behind my right ear filled with moisture and caused me to lose my balance when I knelt. There was an operation to be had for this syndrome, but the cure left you deaf on one side of your head, so I unconditionally refused to be operated on. I was told, with no small veneer of varnish, that I would have to learn to live with it. Fair enough, I managed to get along quite well without kneeling, and by telling only those who were entitled to know of this problem. Most of those people thought of it as an unimportant foible. My heavenly Father, they little knew!

There I stood, enclosed by ruined arches, on ground that echoed to sandalled feet in the distant past, and apropos to absolutely nothing, I was stricken with an overwhelming desire to kneel down. I gave myself some sound advice, but, like Alice of the fairy tale, I did not take it. Finding something substantial to hang on to, I lowered my hulk to my knees. Perspiration ran down my face and my heart thumped as loud as the bell of Newgate. How long it was since my giddy spells had ceased to plague me, I could not tell. It would have been days, it might have been months or even years.

I could never find the answers to my multitude of why's and wherefore's, so I can say with truth that it was not a miracle that happened to me that night, but kneeling there, in a perfectly normal way, those lovely ruins around me, perfectly still, and the dark blue sky ablaze with stars, Harvington conveyed a message to me that sent that warm glow through me, that love which had endured for half a century.

That message cured my reluctance to visit the love of my life, for at Fountains Abbey, fascinating as the remains were, they were cold to touch and the very atmosphere was laden with the serenity of a dead and distant past.

I closed my eyes and held out my hands, and a flight of fancy carried me back to walls of red, Elizabethan bricks, breathing and warm in the sunshine.

Harvington! No longer abandoned, attacked on all sides by the merciless hand of time, but a gem to be preserved in a shining chain of shrines, little oases of peace and promise in a fast-changing world.

With bowed head, I resolved that Harvington should be my next shrine to visit, but it seemed that Harvington was not ready then to receive its off-white pilgrim for so many events got in the way of this sort of reunion, but the desire to write a book about the house never left me. It seemed as if the work of restoring was taking place in my soul as well as at Harvington!

Chapter 10

Venice

THE NIGHT grew cold, but I still stood on the roof clutching the railings, face pointing in the direction where the top storeys of a tall block of council flats could be seen towering above a sea of intervening rooftops. It was one of the many blocks replacing the hovels in the slum clearance, but this particular pile was special to me because it was standing over the place where my mother's little cook-shop used to be.

Mother had been dead for ten years and my stepfather had died several years before her. Mother had spent her last years with me, but in spite of a light veneer of cheerfulness, she missed her miseries in the life she had shared with her third spouse.

Poor old man, whatever his faults, he loved his children, and he spent many an afternoon at the living room window above the cook-shop, which gave him a view of the entire length of the street opposite, hoping so desperately, longing so eagerly, to see a familiar figure approaching the shop to visit him. But they never came. Yet, when a thick November fog carried him off, they all turned up at his funeral crying their eyes out and carrying the most exotic blooms they could obtain.

Daybreak began to lighten the sky. I recalled my first memory of Venice. Beautiful Venice, pathetic in her old age, shimmering in the mists of early morning, reflected in the water of the lagoon like some city from heaven itself.

A day or two after my visit to Fountains Abbey, I had received a letter from an Italian acquaintance of mine, inviting me to go to Venice as governess to a delicate boy of ten.

Did I say 'inviting'? Now I stand on my piece of enlightening roof, reviewing the past in its true perspective. My friend did not so much as 'invite' me to take up the post, but 'beseech' me to do it.

That boy, he told me, one Mario by name, was beyond control, and there was not another man or woman to be found who would take up the challenge. What his actual brand of naughtiness was, my friend was unable to say, but he assured me that his tantrums were way out of this world.

He gave an embellishment of Mario's deeds of evil and a rather supercilious comment on the child's health, and since he had three strapping sons of his own – Mario was an only child – I felt a kind of anger inside which made me take up the challenge. So I left for Venice as soon as all the necessary arrangements were complete.

Mario and company occupied a vast apartment on the first floor of an erstwhile ducal palace. The handsome ceilings, gently glowing in a riot of colour and style of the old Renaissance art, with here and there a big bit of Baroque influence butting in, apropos of nothing in particular, the shining mosaics that adorned the walls and the tessellated patterns on the floors were enough to take one's breath away if the full beauty of the place was not suffocated by the opulence cramping its style. Miles of crimson carpet, heavy plush curtains and cushy-cushy cushions.

Venice was truly a dream of a city, made up of little islands with bridges linking them together to form a city of canals instead of streets. In days gone by, each island had had its own tribune but, after a time, one doge (duke) had ruled the city when it was at its height of prosperity. A city of domes, colourful arcades and exquisite carvings founded by the refugees who had to flee from Attila the Hun, the Ottoman Turks and other barbarians nearer to Rome.

My plan was to take my young charge out to explore the wonderful works of art enclosed within profusely decorated walls. So I asked his mother to give me permission, but she threw up her beautiful hands in horror at the very idea. Mario was present when I made the request, and he stamped and told his dear mother to go to the devil's house and he hoped her toes would drop off on the way.

I had another reason for wanting to take the boy out of the house. I wanted to get him away from his nurse's influence. She was for ever butting in and treating him as if he was ten months old instead of ten years, and she never dodged when he threw objects at her, and never showed one sign of resentment when he tried to kick or punch her.

So, much as I disliked going behind mamma's back, I sought his father's consent. Whenever the signore was about to deliver a homily, he stood up straight as a ramrod, arms akimbo, as if he were addressing a board meeting. When his oratory ran out, he ended with a mighty uncompromising, "NO!"

In his high-pitched, hard-done-by tone, he gave me many good reasons why his boy should not be taken out, and he finished up almost in a shried, "Signorina, please! I standa that bambino's hanka da panka inside da house always sometimes, but 'is damna nonsense outsida the place, sometimes always, by hell, never!"

"But Mario is bored. He could be an ordinary child if he knew what to do with himself. He's being suffocated by the way he is treated like a little hothouse flower.

"Ifa you meana da pansy?"

"No, I do notta meana, I mean, I do not think he is a pansy," I replied, getting way out of my depth, "I was thinking more of hogswort. You should see the nurse's bruises …"

"I should notta see the nurse's bruises. She likes to have them. I give her the lire for eacha da new one."

Sourly, I thought as I turned my heels, he would have cheerfully given a good bonus if I could have shown him a bruise inflicted by his little son and heir.

The following morning, we embarked on a voyage of discovery in a gondola steered by the signor's own private gondolier, who doubtless had been instructed to keep a strict eye on the pair of sightseers. On the Grand Canal we encountered many gondoliers in their gay craft, singing their lungs out, and our fellow, Roberto, joined in until Mario told him in no uncertain voice to, "Shut up!"

Roberto stopped to point out that his 'ighness did not own the canal, then, filling his lungs with air, he resumed his singing in the middle of the rallentando where he had left off, adding a few quivers and quavers ad lib.

I held my breath, waiting for a tantrum, and hoping that the gondolier could swim. I wondered also who was going to pay the fine. It was prohibited to swim in the canal; it did not matter if you were pushed in or whether you fell in: the Venetians who were never happy unless thoroughly miserable, made you pay that fine.

Surprise number one of the day coming up!

Mario stood up and took a stance that would have been the envy of any great singer, and in a voice that outshone Roberto's in volume and tone, my dear little charge burst into song. Nothing from Gilbert and Sullivan's *Gondoliers* (he was not interested in taking 'a pair of sparkling eyes') but he began to render a beautiful old Neapolitan love song. Never had I heard such a glorious tone and pitch issuing from a child's mouth. My jaw was not the only one that dropped open in astonishment. All who were within hearing distance fell silent, enraptured by the suddenness and sheer beauty of the performance.

As we glided towards the Rialto Bridge, I chanced to look up at the balustraded footpath crossing of the bridge, and I saw a sea of appreciative faces smiling and waving at us.

Mario switched off as swiftly as one turns off a light. He put a thumb to his nose and waggled his fingers, yelling out a string of insults, the like of which I had never heard before. Then he flopped down onto his seat and relapsed into a very heavy sulk.

My second surprise of the day was to discover that the child shared my love for ancient bricks and stone, for towers and rooftops and lovely paintings.

It began in the church of Maria della Salute, a magnificent Baroque masterpiece, created by Baldassare Longhena, at the southern end of the canal. Venice is crammed with beautiful churches, but La Salute is the queen of them all. Built as a church to commemorate the end of a horrible plague of

1679, she seems to welcome all the perplexed, the sick at heart and the plain, ordinary bewitched under her gleaming dome. The plague of 1679 was not the only one that seemed to have come to an end; Mario, from that day when we visited La Salute, no longer being the plague of my life. He did not change overnight, but his sudden profound interest in buildings proved to be permanent, and his obsession with paintings and frescoes, together with the exquisite art of the long-gone stuccadoras, seemed to overpower the volcano of boredom burning and active within his small frame.

St. Mark's Square – the great basilica of Saint Mark guarding the evangelist's relics, stolen and brought to Venice from Alexandria, the pink and white façade with its long colonnade of rounded arches of the doge's palace, the library with its most ornate ceiling – opened up a new world of wonder to the scrap of a boy who seemed to be struck dumb by the beauty surrounding him on all sides. He must have seen it all before, but like many people with trees: they knew what they looked like in a vague way, but they had never actually seen one.

This was the case with Mario. He stared, he prodded, and he pried, and on that first day out, he found himself. It was in the breathtaking Church of I Frari, with the Assumption of the Virgin Mary, perhaps Titian's masterpiece of his many paintings. The beautiful portrayal of the mother of Christ hanging above the High Altar, set against a backdrop of tremendous arched windows reaching from the dome to just the level of the altar, forming a mighty arc of light with the gold of the sun mingling with the glowing colours of the gems in the altar panel. It was like standing in the middle of a large soap bubble, and just as fragile, for my moment of wonder was shattered by a burst of abuse from the sacristan. This great big fellow was roaring like a tiger because my precious little charge had climbed over the altar rails, dashed on to the sanctuary and was hoisting himself up on to the archbishop's throne so that he could get a better view of Titian's Assumption.

The little horror refused to get down from the chair and let out a stream of blue abuse in pure Gondolian that left the sacristan speechless. The child, however, stood enraptured after his outburst as he studied the lovely painting and there was no doubt in my mind that Mario had found his niche.

He decided that he would become a painter, he told me as we made tracks for our Roberto and the gondola. I was not surprised when he added that Titian was the best of all painters who had ever lived. It fitted! Titian away from his paint pots was very mean, so history will have it. He was mean and as tight as a fish's behind, and so was his latest admirer, and heaven only knew, that was watertight!

When Roberto finally ferried us home, he was not in the best of tempers because we had dallied so long in the church of I Frari looking at a picture "'Angin' uppa there fora the 'undreds of years anda likely to 'anga for another day! Anda aparta froma thata, thata sacristano wasa 'is brother-ina-the-law, anda he woulda no doubta tella the counta – oughta notta the signorina – to know thata to allowa da boyo to putta da foota where-a da bishop sittas his assio, wasa da bigga sin? And 'e had notta 'adda 'is dinner yet anda thata wasa da worsest." Here he almost broke down, but I was suddenly satisfied, for Mario, when he left home that morning, had a pair of large eyes like two burnt holes in a blanket, but when we returned to the fold, they were two pools of light shining with anticipation.

That day marked the beginning of a new epoch in the stormy life of the boy, for one of the misfits had found his niche in life; as for me, I was still to complete my quest, for only then would I discover my niche. Why this boy became so special to me over the years is a mystery. When he had one of his off days, I could have cheerfully murdered him, like when on two occasions he was fished out of the Grand Canal, and the afternoon when he bit Roberto on the ear. That made history the length and breadth of the Lagoon!

Venice was crammed with buildings, cheek by jowl with the many and varied influences of bygone builders. When we had had our fill of the magic which Venice had on offer, I was allowed to take Mario to Florence and, this proving to be an unqualified success, it was not long before, in August 1978, we saw the magnificence that was Rome.

We had seen the work of the Bellini brothers, Veronese and Tintoretto, and gazed in wonder at Titian's art; we had admired golden staircases and unbelievably ornate ceilings above them, and then, when we thought we had seen everything, we stood in the Sistine Chapel, beneath Michelangelo's ceiling and frescoes: God's creation of Adam.

Whatever passed through the child's mind, I never found out. As for me, memory carried me back to Harvington Hall when I looked up at a great man's painting of the Almighty, for as a child of ten myself, I stood outside the door of a lonely and forsaken little chapel in an abandoned house, afraid to go inside because of a God of stern expression and flowing white hair.

This painting of God was very much like the God of my childhood, but the outflung arm was bestowing a blessing on Adam, and the face of the Creator shone with love and pity.

I recalled My Lord standing at the end of the bridge spanning the moat with the sun shining on his silvery hair, with one hand holding his breviary, the other stretched out to welcome a small ragamuffin. The lump that came to my throat whenever I thought about him, was suddenly threatening to suffocate me.

So we left the chapel in silence, and gave the inhabitants of Rome something to grin about, for we must have looked an odd couple, the nosey little boy poking and prying into places that were private and sacred, while his companion seemed to be bemused at the magnificence surrounding her.

Somebody asked him if I was his grandmother, and he replied quite seriously that I was not his dear, darling grandmother, I was only the Queen of England, and I was good at minding my own business. He was preparing to spit, and I only just managed to head him off in time. No camel in this world could outshine him at this delicate art!

In spite of its immense proportions and its grandeur, we felt that St. Peter's was a cosy place to pray in. It was so homely in spite of the great statues and gallons of gold leaf paint. Mothers took up odd corners to sit in and feed their infants. We heard a flower-seller bitterly complaining that they were putting too much salt in the holy water, so the flowers she stood in the stoups died really dead when she stood them in to liven them up. Our crowning laugh on our first visit was to see two old tramps sitting opposite each other on the floor, with their bare feet stretched out in front of them, and each gentleman of the road was most industriously scratching the soles of the other's feet. The expression on their faces was heavenly. Mario beamed at them as he showered lire over them. "Scratch away," he told them in the tone of a benevolent old uncle. "Does your mother know you are out?"

When finally I left Venice to return to the South Lambeth Road, I was accompanied by my little shadow, who went off in a roof-shattering tantrum and would have done himself or his papa a mischief, if that poor hysterical man had not given way to him and let him spend a few weeks in England with me.

My head spun as I compared the beautiful home in Venice with my humble flat with its leaking roof and sloping floors. I told myself complacently that Mario would soon bellow to go back to papa and nursie. I was quite wrong. Children never cease to amaze me. He took to Lambeth as a duck takes to water. For a day or two, he was just a hanger-on, when he joined the Wilcox Market gang, but before the end of a week, he was the leader. He was the big boss.

We went to Paris on a short trip so that he could visit the Louvre Palace and I could climb the Eiffel Tower. For a week we went to Bruges where he inspected the Memling Museum and I climbed the Belfry. Together we climbed a hillside in Lourdes to follow the beautiful Stations of the Cross. The twelfth station, Jesus Dies on the Cross, was high on the hillside, and the last red-gold rays of the sunset rested on the figure on the cross. I looked down at the boy and, to my surprise, I saw tears in his eyes, the first real tears I had seen him shed. I did not ask him what was troubling him, he would not have told me anyway. I suppose it was because his parents were coming for him to take him up north to his abbey school.

And so I said farewell to my charge, thinking that would be the last I would see of him. But I was wrong. As his schooldays passed, he kept in touch and spent short holidays at the flat, and I was always invited to special functions at the abbey.

He never became a famous artist, neither did he become renowned as an opera-singer. He gave his life to God, by joining the community that had taken him on where I had left off.

He came to see me to say "Goodbye", and when there was nothing else left to be said, he looked into my face and said very seriously, "*Aveccia donna,* I went to see Harvington Hall by myself. It is a funny-looking house really, but it is alive in its spirit. It is asking you to write your book. Write it, *aveccia donna.* Write it."

Afterword

Almost seventy years after she first explored it, Emily Rose Martin returned to Harvington Hall with her book written. Nowadays the Hall is often full of off-white angels aged 10, because under the National Curriculum that is the age at which children are required to learn about the Tudors and day after day coach-loads of them clatter across the bridge and into the courtyard for their own first encounters with this unique building. Its condition in 1921 is now an historic memory, recorded in this book and in the old sepia photographs that illustrate it. The muddy wilderness beyond the courtyard is now a garden where in summer Shakespearian comedies are performed against a backdrop of trees, water and Elizabethan brickwork. The missing Great Staircase has

Archbishop Ilsley

been replaced by a copy in English oak, whose balusters of 1947 echo the painted shadow of 1600. The Great Chamber is used for wedding receptions and concerts of early music. And above the heraldic over-mantel, which replaces the original torn out in 1855, is a Latin inscription from Isaiah 58: *Aedificabuntur in te deserta saeculorum:* 'What was ancient and abandoned, you shall rebuild'.

Rosie was awed by "My Lord" and only later did she discover that he was Archbishop Edward Ilsley of Birmingham. It was in 1921, just before his stay at Harvington Hall, that he retired at the age of 83. He died in 1927.